CB126732

American Inside Out Evolution

Workbook

Advanced

SUE KAY
JON HIRD
CERI JONES
TANIA BASTOW
VAUGHAN JONES
AMANDA JEFFRIES

macmillan education

Macmillan Education
Companies and representatives throughout the world
American Inside Out Evolution. Workbook Advanced

Adapted by Petter Maggs and Catherine Smith
Content Writers: Ben Naismith, James Michael Ubriaco and Lavaughn John
Macmillan is a registered trademark.
First edition published 2018

ISBN: 978-607-473-639-7

Based on New American Inside Out Workbook Advanced
D.R. © Macmillan Publishers, S.A. de C.V. 2010
Published under license from Macmillan Publishers Ltd.

Director of Languages Brazil: Patrícia Souza
Editorial Manager: Patricia Muradas
Art Editor: Jean Aranha
Content Editors: Cintia Zaitune and Larissa Vannucci
Digital Editor: Ana Paula Girardi
Concept design: Martha Tadaieski
Page make-up: Figurattiva Editorial
Illustrations: Gustavo Gialuca
Graphic Production: Kelly Gobbo and Tatiane Romano
Proofreaders: Edward Willson and Larissa Vazquez
Photographic research: Cintia Zaitune, Denis Araujo, Jean Aranha and Marcia Sato
Image Processing: Denis Araujo and Jean Aranha
Cover concept and design: Jean Aranha
Cover photo: Steve Keller | Dreamstime.com

The authors and publishers would like to thank the following for permission to reproduce their photographs:
iStock / grandriver p6; iStock / mactrunk p6; iStock / unpict p8; iStock / lenta p9; iStock / LeS_ p13; iStock / GCShutter p16; iStock / PeskyMonkey p16; iStock / Vesnaandjic p16; iStock / Pekic p18; iStock / Ridofranz p27; iStock / Kiuikson p27; iStock / nilimage p27; iStock / monkeybusinessimages p31; iStock / Kyryl Gorlov p40; iStock / Martin Dimitrov p44; iStock / djedzura p44; iStock / PeopleImages p45; iStock / Sitthiphong p45; iStock / gradyreese p45; iStock / vchal p45; iStock / LightFieldStudios p45; iStock / Petar Chernaev p46; iStock / UberImages p46; iStock / twinsterphoto p46; iStock / PeopleImages p46; iStock / kali9 p48; iStock / iStock / Geber86 p48; iStock / PeopleImages p48; iStock / Ivanko_Brnjakovic p48; iStock / pixdeluxe p48; iStock / Wavebreakmedia p48; iStock / tuk69tuk p48; iStock / Maxiphoto p49; iStock / Sladic p49; iStock / AZemdega p49; iStock / Petar Chernaev p49; iStock / monkeybusinessimages p49; iStock / zefart p49; iStock / indukas p49;

The team of publishers of the series is especially thankful to Cristina Neville and her team for all the support throughout all the stages of the editing process of this publication.

CANIEM No. 2275

Macmillan Publishers S.A. de C.V. Insurgentes Sur 1886
Col. Florida, CP 01030
Álvaro Obregón
Ciudad de México
Tel: +52 (55) 5482 2200
elt@grupomacmillan.com

www.grupomacmillan.com
www.macmillan.com.mx
www.macmillanenglish.com

Printed in Brazil

This book was printed in June, 2018 by: Eskenazi Indústria Gráfica Ltda, Avenida Miguel Frias Vasconcelos, 1023 - Jaguaré - São Paulo - SP.

Contents

1 Conversation

GRAMMAR

1 **Add the adverbials in parentheses to the sentences below. Sometimes more than one position is possible.**

a I talk to my grandmother on the phone. (at least once a month)

a Eavesdropping can get you into big trouble! (at work)
Eavesdropping at work can get you into big trouble! / Eavesdropping can get you into big trouble at work!

b I had a really interesting conversation with a complete stranger. (recently)

____

____

c I hate people who talk about themselves all the time. (endlessly)

____

____

d I overheard the most incredible conversation on the bus! (the other day)

____

____

e I talk to my grandmother on the phone. (at least once a month)

____

____

f I tried to call my boyfriend, but he didn't answer the phone. (last night)

____

____

2 **Add adverbials to the following sentences so that they are true for you.**

a I love people who talk to me. (add an adverbial saying how)

____

____

b I meet up with my friends to relax and hang out. (add adverbials saying how often and where)

____

____

c I had a really long talk with my best friend. (add an adverbial saying when)

____

____

3 **Rewrite the following sentences, changing the position of the adverbial in bold so that the meaning of the sentence changes.**

1 a I had really wanted my parents to meet my boyfriend **earlier on in the day**.
b *Earlier on in the day, I had really wanted my parents to meet my boyfriend.*

2 a **Frankly**, she just didn't answer the question.
b ______________________________

____

3 a I really regretted asking Jane to come to the party **later**.
b ______________________________

____

4 a I'd just talk to him about it **normally**.
b ______________________________

____

5 a **Only** Jack knew how to read Arabic.
b ______________________________

____

6 a I think she **sometimes** finds my obsession with neatness annoying.
b ______________________________

____

4 **Match the sentences below with the correct sentence (*a* or *b*) in each pair in Exercise 3.**

1 But by the end of the afternoon, I had changed my mind. I knew it would be a huge mistake! [*b*]
2 It would have been much better if she'd told the truth. [ ]
3 But by then it was too late. The invitations had been sent and there was nothing I could do about it. [ ]
4 But we've both been away on holiday, so I had to email him. [ ]
5 Unfortunately, he didn't know how to speak it. [ ]
6 Only sometimes? I think it annoys her pretty much all the time! [ ]

5 **Underline the correct form of the verb.**

Well, I (1) **<u>was standing</u> / had stood** in line at the checkout in the grocery store the other day when I overheard a really interesting conversation. One woman (2) **was telling / had told** another woman about her boyfriend. She (3) **was going / had gone** on and on about how wonderful he was. How he (4) **was always taking / had always taken** care of her, cooking and cleaning and buying romantic gifts. I (5) **was beginning / have been beginning** to feel jealous, when suddenly the woman's cell phone rang. "Yes, honey," she answered. "No honey, of course, honey, right away. Yes, I (6) **'ve bought / 'd been buying** some beer ... yes, I (7) **'ve remembered / 'm remembering** your sports magazine ... no, of course I don't mind if Ben and Dan come over ... Yes, yes, I (8) **'ll be getting / 'll have got** the food ready while you (9) **'re watching / 've watched** soccer ... No, no, don't worry, you take it easy." "As always," she added under her breath as she hung up. Of course, everyone else (10) **had been listening / had listened** too, and at that point we all looked away, desperately trying to look like we (11) **hadn't heard / weren't hearing** a word and (12) **were just waiting / had just waited** to pay for our groceries.

02 Listen and check.

6 There are mistakes in the sentences below. Find and correct them.

a Who would have thought he could do such a thing? He's always ~~been being~~ such a quiet person.
been ______

b This time next week, I'll have laid on a golden beach, far away from everything.
______

c If I had been born in a different country, I might be having a completely different childhood.
______

d I've never really been understanding why some people don't enjoy traveling abroad.
______

e He's been working on this project for such a long time. I'm glad he finally gets some recognition for it.
______

7 Complete the sentences so that they are true for you. Use perfect, progressive, or perfect progressive verbs where possible.

a This time next week, I ______

b By the time I'm 50, I ______

c I'd been standing ______, when ______

d I've always wanted to know why ______

e My life might have been very different if ______

f I've spent a long time trying to ______, but ______

VOCABULARY

1 Complete the sentences with the adjectives in the box.

~~animated~~ bizarre frustrating hilarious in-depth lengthy pointless

a The discussion was really *animated*, with voices raised and people shouting, but in excitement, not in anger.

b His opening speech was ______ . We haven't laughed so much for a long time.

c It was so ______ trying to explain the problem to him. I didn't know what else to say to make him understand.

d The discussion we had on the future of the company was ______ and well-researched, and we felt that we'd made some progress.

e I thought the meeting was ______ . The management team clearly had no intention of listening to our arguments.

f It was a ______ conversation, but we did eventually come to an agreement.

g I got caught up in this totally ______ conversation with a complete stranger. I swear, I have no idea what she was talking about!

2 Replace the words in bold with a verb or expression from the box in the correct form.

always have something to say be on the same wavelength butt in drone on and on flow ~~get across~~ hog hunt around for

a It was really difficult to **convey** the underlying concept. *get across*

b We get along really well. We seem to **share similar views and values.** ______

c The conversation **was really easy and comfortable** and the time flew. ______

d Excuse me, I hope you don't mind me **interrupting** like this. ______

e His lectures are so boring. He just **talks and talks** in a monotone voice. ______

f I don't enjoy talking to Rod. He always **dominates** the conversation and never listens to what other people have to say. ______

g There was a long, embarrassing silence and I was forced to **think of** a new topic to bring the conversation back to life! ______

h Jose is really interesting. He **is never at a loss for words**, no matter who he's talking to.
______

3 Underline the correct word.

a The ability to be tactful is a great <u>**skill**</u> / **skilled** / **skillfulness**.

b She works so **efficient** / **efficiency** / **efficiently** with her new computer that she gets the job done in half the time.

c He's completely lacking in **competence** / **competent** / **competently** and can't do the job properly.

d I'm looking for a job where I can **fulfillment** / **fulfill** / **fulfilling** my ambition to write.

e It's very **satisfaction** / **satisfying** / **satisfied** when people congratulate you on making a good presentation.

f He doesn't have any **consideration** / **consider** / **considerate** for anyone else, he just does what he wants and expects everyone to go along with him.

g Do you think getting that report finished by five o'clock is really **achievement** / **achievable** / **unachievable**?

4 **Complete the sentences with the correct form of the words in parentheses.**

a She's a very ___considerate___ person and always thinks about the needs of the people around her. (consider)

b I really don't think your work is __________ . You're going to have to make much more of an effort if you hope to pass the exam. (satisfy)

c It really is one of the most __________ jobs I've ever had. It's great to see the students making so much progress. (fulfill)

d Your son's worked hard this semester and should feel very proud of his __________ . (achieve)

e The shortage of __________ workers is a big problem right now. (skill)

f That's not a very __________ way of working. I'm sure you could do the job much faster. (efficiency)

g He's a very __________ driver. He'll have no problem getting his license. (competence)

PRONUNCIATION

1 03 **Listen to the same sentence being said twice. Which sentence (*a* or *b*) is said in a normal tone, and which is said in an angry tone? Write N for normal and A for angry.**

a You forgot to do the laundry. ☐

b You forgot to do the laundry. ☐

2 04 **Listen to the sentences. Does the speaker use a normal tone or an angry tone? Write *N* for normal and *A* for angry.**

a This place is a mess!

b Could you turn that down, please?

c I guess you'd rather watch TV, huh?

d I don't want to disturb you or anything.

e Are you going to put those away?

f Let's discuss this later.

a	b	c	d	e	f
N					

3 **Listen again and repeat the sentences. Use an angry tone or a normal tone.**

WRITING

Writing an email of complaint

Paragraph organization

1 **Read the review below for a restaurant that has just opened. Then answer these questions:**

a What kind of food does it serve?

b What is the atmosphere like?

c Is it expensive?

Restaurant of the Week

If you haven't been to Casa Paco yet, then you don't know what you're missing. This cozy little tapas bar has just opened on East 5th Street. It is set out like a farmhouse kitchen, with simple pine furniture, traditional Spanish earthenware, and a huge fire blazing in the grate. The atmosphere is laid-back and friendly, and the clientele a mixture of students, young professionals, and friends of the Spanish couple who runs the place. The menu offers an incredibly wide selection of dishes, ranging from classic tortillas to the exquisite daily specials conjured up on the spot by Paco and his wife, Laura.

2 **You were so impressed by the review that you decided to book a table at Casa Paco for a surprise birthday party for a very close friend. The evening was a total disaster. Look at the list below and choose four or five of the problems to describe your evening.**

- half the dishes on the menu were unavailable
- the waiters were surly
- the service was incredibly slow
- the restaurant was crowded
- you had to wait half an hour for your table
- you were expected to share a table with another group of people
- some of the dishes were cold by the time they arrived on the table
- it was very expensive - definitely overpriced!

The quality of the food is superb, a difficult task with such an amazing range of delicacies to prepare. We tried more than fifteen dishes between us, each one better than the last. The shellfish is so fresh you can still smell the ocean, the meat is succulent and done to a turn, and the desserts are quite something to behold. It can get really busy on weekends, but the staff is never flustered, and it's always service with a smile. Maybe the secret lies in the smooth Latin sounds playing softly in the background. All this for the price of your average pizza. If you're looking for a new eating experience, head for Casa Paco. You won't be disappointed!

3 **You are going to write an email of complaint to the magazine the review appeared in. Before you do, read an email written by another angry reader, complaining about a recent review printed in the same magazine, and answer these questions.**

a What was the review for?

b Why is the writer of the email so angry?

www.restaurantoftheweek.com

Dear Editor,

Having recently read a rave review in your magazine for the latest John Howard movie, I immediately called my local movie theater and booked three tickets for myself and two friends. We were looking forward to a great evening, but I'm sad to say that we were grievously disappointed.

Your reviewer had described the movie as a "fun-packed adventure story" and we had gone in the hope of taking our minds off the stresses and strains of a hard week at work. It turned out that the movie was far from light-hearted. The plot was depressing – the story of a young man fighting a life-threatening disease, the movie itself long and very slow-moving, and the ending was one of the saddest I've ever seen. In brief, the review was totally misleading.

The movie itself is very good, but I would only recommend it for those looking for a real tear-jerker. I'm sorry to say that after such an awful experience I don't think I'll ever be able to trust your reviews again. I suggest you take more care in the future or you will lose more loyal readers like myself.

Yours disappointedly,

Rob Walters

4 **In which paragraph (1–3) is the writer**

a referring to the future?

b contrasting the movie and the review?

c explaining the reason for writing the letter?

5 **Follow the paragraph structure in the model email above and write your own email of complaint to the magazine about their restaurant review. Read the email again and underline any useful language that you think you could use in your email. You should write approximately 200 words.**

2 Taste

GRAMMAR

1 **Underline all the noun phrases in this text which have three words or more.**

We had a great dinner. Lucy cooked for us, and she's a fantastic cook. We started with some great little smoked salmon canapés. They were absolutely delicious! Then we had some cold cucumber soup and tiny little fingers of crisp toast. The main course was incredible; you really should have seen it. She brought out a tray of fresh lobsters and served them with a very simple green salad. I thought I couldn't possibly eat any more, but when she brought out the dessert, a home-made chocolate mousse, it was just too good to resist!

2 **Reorder these words and phrases to form complex noun phrases that describe different types of drinks.**

a piping hot / straight from the pot / coffee / a cup of / strong

a cup of strong piping hot coffee straight from the pot

b citrus / a mixture of / with just a touch of lemon / juices / tangy

____

c and a slice of lemon / water / with a couple of fresh mint leaves / ice-cold / a glass of

____

d full-fat / straight from the refrigerator / a glass of / milk / fresh

____

e hot / on top / a steaming cup of / with a dollop of cream / chocolate

____

3 **Write the words in italics in the correct order.**

a a tub of vanilla ice cream with *chocolate dark delicious* flakes

delicious dark chocolate

b a bowl of *bean Mexican spicy* soup

____

c the smell of *black Italian strong* coffee

____

d her *ceramic exquisite hand-painted* bowl

____

e a *large red shiny* apple

____

f half a dozen *blue speckled tiny* quail eggs

____

g a *china new beautiful* tea set

____

4 **Write detailed descriptions of the following things. Use at least three adjectives each time.**

a something you ate for breakfast today

____

b a typical regional dish from your town

____

c the last thing you had to drink

____

d your favorite comfort food

____

e a kind of food you really don't enjoy

____

f the dish you most enjoy cooking

____

g something your mother cooks

____

5 **Rewrite the sentences, fronting the words in bold.**

a The rain came **down** and washed the dust away.
Down came the rain and washed the dust away.

b The sound of raised voices could be heard **in** the kitchen.
____

c Half a dozen fishing boats were **bobbing** gently on the water.
____

d The name of the restaurant was **The Western Isle**.
____

e The best words to describe it are **homey**, simple, and down-to-earth.
____

f The days of peace and harmony were **long** gone.
____

g We didn't really know **what** had happened.
____

h We had no idea **when** she'd be coming back.
____

PRONUNCIATION

Look at the words in the box. Write them alongside the appropriate stress pattern. The first one has been done for you.

~~cauliflower~~ convenience criticism delicious exquisite intricate microwave refreshing selection strawberries vegetables

a □□□□ cauliflower
b □□□ ______________________________
c □□□ ______________________________

05 **Listen and check.**

VOCABULARY

1 **Complete the sentences with the words in the box. You may need to make some changes to the verbs.**

chug clientele GPS reverie ~~thriving~~ thrust

a What had once been a thriving fishing community was now just a collection of abandoned cottages.

b She looked up from her ______________ to see that the platform had cleared and her train had departed.

c The restaurant had a very cosmopolitan ______________ and a lively atmosphere.

d He punched the address into the ______________ , sat back in the driver's seat, and thought of the long trip ahead.

e They looked in dismay at the fuel gauge as the car ______________ slowly to a halt on the side of the road.

f The man walked up to me, ______________ a letter into my hand, and then rushed away.

2 **Replace a word or phrase in each sentence with a word or phrase from the box.**

batter blared out exquisite ~~homey~~ pricey thriving

a It's a simple, comfortable, and ~~informal~~ restaurant run by a family. homey

b The food was fantastic – perfectly cooked and beautifully presented. ______________

c Our meal was spoiled by the music which played loudly from a loudspeaker above our table.
____

d That restaurant's way too expensive. Let's find somewhere else to eat. ______________

e He runs a successful restaurant just outside Rome.
____

f The shrimp was coated in a mixture of flour, milk, and egg whites, and then deep fried.
____

3 **Match the sentence beginnings (a–f) with their endings (1–6).**

a I think he has great taste in clothes;
b I think that joke was in very bad taste;
c It's a place with something for all tastes,
d Fresh fruit from Brazil has so much taste;
e The main course was very tasty, but
f I'm not quite sure about the taste;

1 it's a joy to go shopping at the markets there.
2 it was offensive and certainly not funny.
3 maybe it needs a little more garlic.
4 he always looks so stylish and elegant.
5 where the entire family will find something to do.
6 I was disappointed with the dessert.

a	b	c	d	e	f
4					

4 **Complete the sentences with words formed from *taste*.**

a Our meal in that new restaurant was awful. The food was completely tasteless.
b The choice of colors was very ____________. It was obvious that whoever owned the house had a good eye for colors.
c The beer festival normally starts very seriously, with everyone ____________ the different beers and commenting on them.
d I thought the whole wedding ceremony was ____________. I mean, who in their right mind would have a priest dressed as Elvis Presley?

5 **Use one word to complete each sentence. The first letter has been given to help you.**

a We both apologized to each other later, but the incident left a bad taste in my mouth.
b Black olives are definitely an a____________ taste. I didn't like them as a child, but I love them now.
c I get along really well with my new roommate. We s____________ the same taste in everything!
d I don't understand people who listen to rock music first thing in the morning. But I guess there's no a ____________ for taste!

6 **Underline the best alternative in the conversations (a–d).**

a

Ruby: Have you heard? Jo's thinking about quitting her job.
Tom: (1) **I guess you're right.** / **That can't be right!** I was talking to her the other night and she seemed really happy with her job.
Ruby: (2) **That may be, but** / **I know, it's awful,** she told me that she and Greg are going to open a restaurant.

b

Tom: We went to Jo and Greg's new restaurant last night.
Ruby: And?
Tom: Well, I hate to say it, but the service was really slow and the food was terrible!
Ruby: (3) **I rest my case.** / **I know, it's awful, isn't it?** We went a couple of nights ago and I was really embarrassed for them.

c

Jo: The customers have been complaining about the service again. They say it's really slow.
Greg: But (4) **that's garbage!** / **I guess you're right!** We're all working as quickly as we can and no one's had to wait more than about ten minutes.
Jo: Well, (5) **I think you'll find that** / **that may be, but** the couple in the corner has been waiting for more than half an hour.

d

Jack: This is one of the worst restaurants I've ever been to!
Ella: (6) **Oh, I don't know,** / **I guess you're right,** the staff is friendly and the decor's nice ... Ah, here's the fish ... Oh, no, it's cold!
Jack: And it's only half-cooked! (7) **That's garbage!** / **I rest my case!**
Ella: (8) **I guess you're right.** / **No way!**

06 **Listen and check.**

LISTENING

1 07 **Cover the listening script on the right and listen to four stories about people's experiences in restaurants. Then choose an appropriate title for each one.**

a Open all hours
b A quiet night out?
c A fishy tale
d A free lunch

story	1	2	3	4
title				

2 **Listen again. In which story is there:**

a a case of mistaken identity?
b an illness?
c a violent incident?
d a generous gesture?

story	1	2	3	4
topic				

3 **Which stories might these sentences come from?**

a It's great to see you. You know, Luis was asking about you. He was wondering if you were still working on that translation project. ☐
b Don't worry. I eat here all the time. Let me order. ☐
c I've had enough of this! I'm not going to stand for it any longer! ☐
d There are some drinks behind the bar and the music is by the stereo. ☐

4 **Complete the sentences with the words in the box. You will need to use some of them more than once.**

at on to up

a He insisted _____ ordering.
b I'm allergic _____ shellfish.
c I noticed a couple waving _____ me.
d He put _____ a special night for us.
e As the evening went _____ , we all started dancing.
f At twelve o'clock Juan came over _____ me.
g He asked us to lock everything _____ when we left.
h He started shouting _____ the waiter.
i He ended _____ with his face in my soup.

Check your answers in the listening script.

1 On our first date, my boyfriend took me to a really fancy restaurant. Clearly wanting to impress me, he insisted on ordering, so I said fine, but warned him not to order anything with shellfish in it - I'm allergic to it. I thought I'd made myself perfectly clear about this and that he knew what he was ordering, but obviously he didn't. An hour later I was in an ambulance being rushed to the hospital. I could hardly breathe. My boyfriend looked rather embarrassed, sitting by my side holding the oxygen mask to my face.

2 I was in a restaurant with my wife one evening and I couldn't help noticing a couple waving at me from a different table. Eventually the man came over, said hello, and started talking about something I knew nothing about. He then said, "Goodbye, Pablo," and sat back down at his table. We finished our meal and asked for the check. The waiter told us that the man at the other table, who'd since left, had paid it for us. I'm absolutely certain I'd never met him before in my life.

3 I used to live in this little village in Mexico, and each Friday my friends and I would go down to the port to eat at our favorite restaurant. The owner, Juan, was a great guy, and when I told him my friend was coming over from the US, he said he'd put on a special night for us. And he certainly did. It was amazing, and the food was out of this world. As the evening went on, we all started dancing, and when it got to twelve o'clock, Juan came over to me. I thought he was going to ask us to leave, but instead he gave me the keys to the restaurant and told me we could stay as long as we liked as long as we didn't forget to lock everything up!

4 We were sitting in a restaurant in Miami when we noticed three guys at the next table who were obviously getting frustrated because the service was so slow. Suddenly, one of them stood up and started shouting at the waiter and telling him to hurry up with his food. The waiter answered back rather rudely and the next minute everything went crazy. One of the guys ran into the kitchen and started a fight with a chef and the other two began fighting with the waiters. It was like something out of a cowboy movie, with bodies flying everywhere! Finally, one of the chefs came flying across our table and ended up with his face in my soup. The crazy thing is, they still made us pay the check and we weren't even offered a discount.

3 City

GRAMMAR

1 Complete each sentence by choosing two possible answers from the box.

appear ~~appears~~ believed evidence hardly any little proof proved recognized seem ~~seems~~ shown

a It *appears* / *seems* that the population of many modern industrialized cities is beginning to decline.

b There is ______ / ______ doubt that in the future we will have to take radical action to control traffic congestion in our cities.

c It is generally ______ / ______ that living in cities with a population of over a million people can be detrimental to our health.

d There is little ______ / ______ that the levels of toxic pollution in the major cities in the US are beginning to decline.

e It would ______ / ______ that the changes in weather patterns could endanger large urban populations in low-lying land areas due to the rise in sea level.

f It has been ______ / ______ that prolonged exposure to the sun can cause skin cancer.

2 Rewrite these sentences using the words in parentheses.

a Smoking can lead to cancer. (no doubt)
There is no doubt that smoking can lead to cancer.

b Scientists in many countries believe that climate change is the greatest challenge facing our society. (widely) ______

c There is evidence to suggest that the rate of population growth in China is beginning to decrease. (appears) ______

d There is a general feeling that people believe governments are not doing enough about global warming. (would seem) ______

3 Complete the negative and limiting adverbial phrases in the sentences below using *no*, *not*, or *only*.

a The teacher told them that on *no* account were they to leave the school premises.

b ______ after a long wait did we finally get to hear the results of the tests.

c We were told that under ______ circumstances were we to use our cell phones.

d ______ even in summer are there so many tourists to be seen in the town.

e ______ until he'd left college did he really appreciate how much he'd enjoyed being a student.

f In ______ other world capital will you find the same incredible mix of nationalities.

g ______ once in the whole time I knew him did he ever make a mistake in judgment.

h ______ after spending a few months here will you understand how this city survives.

4 Complete the adverbial phrases with the words in the box.

~~after~~ after barely never only rarely seldom sooner

a I realized how much I loved the city only *after* I had left it.

b We had no ______ moved in to our new house than our troubles began.

c The local people were not ______ rude to us, but they also ignored the children.

d We had ______ imagined that people could be so hostile.

e We made our first friend only ______ two months.

f We very ______ saw him, however, and life was still lonely.

g The children had ______ been so quiet before.

h We decided to go back to the city. We had ______ put up a "For Sale" sign when the people began to be friendly towards us!

08 **Listen and check.**

5 Rewrite the sentences from Exercise 4 so that they begin with the adverbial phrases you completed.

a Only after I had left the city did I realize how much I loved it.

b ______________________________

c ______________________________

d ______________________________

e ______________________________

f ______________________________

g ______________________________

h ______________________________

PRONUNCIATION

1 Look at the sentences below. Underline all the examples of the sound /ɔ/.

a Its beauty is not as awe-inspiring as other cities.

b Everyone seems to stay out late, as though some unwritten law forbade sleeping before dawn.

c You're constantly jostled by hawkers and hordes of tourists.

d You can find pockets of another time, such as an old wooden house, a kimono shop, or a small inn.

e You might even see an old lady in a traditional dress sweeping the sidewalk outside her home with a straw broom.

f It's the city's hyperactive rush that really draws the people here.

09 Listen and check.

2 Look at the words in the box. Cross out the ones that don't contain the sound /ɔ/.

crowded	dawn	fog	gawk
hall	law	modern	splendor
sprawl	world		

10 Listen and check.

VOCABULARY

1 Match the adjectives (a–f) with their opposites (1–6).

a haphazard — 1 modest
b tacky — 2 unimpressive
c bustling — 3 organized
d soaring — 4 stylish
e in-your-face — 5 sleepy
f awe-inspiring — 6 low-rise

a	b	c	d	e	f
3					

2 Underline the one word in each group which does not collocate with the adjective.

a haphazard: arrangement magazine system
b tacky: clothes decorations meeting
c bustling: family marketplace streets
d soaring: houses mountain tops office buildings
e in-your-face: celebrities talk fashions
f awe-inspiring: performance sight village

3 Complete the sentences with adjectives from Exercises 1 and 2.

a I think the plastic souvenirs some people buy on vacation are really tacky.

b With its 24-hour culture centered on gambling and entertainment, its neon signs, and its brash nature, Las Vegas is one of the world's most __________ cities.

c Arriving in Hong Kong harbor, you're immediately struck by the __________ skyscrapers that stretch as far as the eye can see.

d The streets were __________ with people waiting for the procession to start.

e The city planned the new one-way system in a very __________ way. I kept getting lost and having to ask for directions.

f The first sight of the Andes on a clear day is __________.

4 **Replace the expressions in bold with the expressions in the box. Make any necessary changes to the expressions.**

fall prey to live on top of each other put a finger on something ~~to make way for a new~~ work its magic

a They knocked down the old stadium **in order to put a** shopping mall **in its place**.
to make way for a new shopping mall

b I could never **quite understand** what he saw in her.

______

c They were a family of eight and they **were all crammed in together** in a small two-bedroom apartment.

______

d I **became a victim of** the charms of the street vendors with their beautiful silk scarves and silver jewelry.

______

e I arrived tired and stressed after an eventful trip, but as I sat by the lake, the view of the sun setting on the water **helped me relax**.

______

5 **Solve the anagrams (a–g) and then match them with the definitions (1–7).**

a treets rfeporsmre *street performers* *4*
b hekcc tou ______ ___
c rgoeg ______ ___
d ntar ______ ___
e kawg ta ______ ___
f yihdnal ______ ___
g etasreie ______ ___

1 conveniently
2 places where you can get food
3 a loud and protracted complaint
4 musicians who play or sing on the street
5 to go and see what something's like
6 to watch, look at, or stare at someone
7 to eat an enormous amount of food

6 **Add *do, does,* or *did* to the sentences below. Change the verbs in the original sentences if necessary.**

a I really *did enjoy* ~~enjoyed~~ the movie last night. It's one of the best movies I've ever seen.

b You're right about the new stadium. It looks a little bit out of place.

c Shopping malls are fine if you're looking for convenience, but I think local street markets are much more interesting.

d Our neighbors are really friendly, but they make a lot of noise sometimes!

e My elementary school was really small, but it had an enormous sports field.

f My office is a mess. It really needs a good, thorough reorganization.

7 **Write the words in the correct order.**

a about it / I love most / The thing / is / the dome / .
The thing I love most about it is the dome.

b the sunlight / It's / I love / that / it reflects / the way that / .

______

c from the tower / are / What / the spectacular views / I also like / .

______

d you have to / is that / One thing / pay to / I don't like / go inside the cathedral / .

______

e swaying in the wind / It's / with / the square / its palm trees / I love / that / .

______

f is / I really like / there's always / the fact that / What / a cool ocean breeze / .

______

8 **Write three sentences about a place you particularly like.**

a The thing I ______

b What I ______

c It's the ______

WRITING

Writing a short article
Linkers
Text organization

1 **Read the following text and choose the best discourse marker.**

Hosting the Olympics® is extremely expensive. (1) **Furthermore, / However, / On the other hand,** it can ruin the local environment. (2) **Despite / For instance, / But** greenfield sites and woodlands can be lost to urban development, which means that local residents' quality of life may be diminished. (3) **In addition, / Although / On the other hand,** it can provide a boost to the local economy, generating jobs and trade. (4) **However, / Despite / In addition,** the effects can be all too temporary, leaving a city with unwanted installations and a huge debt to pay. (5) **Nonetheless, / What's more, / For example,** with careful forward planning, most of these problems can be avoided.

2 **Look at the list of changes that can occur in a city when it hosts the Olympic Games.**

a Decide whether you think their effect will be long-term (LT) or short-term (ST).

b Decide which of the changes are benefits (+) and which are drawbacks (-).

1	An increase in pollution and trash	ST	–
2	Improved sports installations		
3	More jobs in the construction industry		
4	Good publicity for the city		
5	Improved roads and airports		
6	Temporary accommodation facilities		
7	An increase in traffic congestion		
8	More facilities for parking cars		
9	Massive increase in number of visitors		
10	An increase in local trade		
11	Security problems		

3 **Read the following task.**

Your city (or a city near you) has made a bid for the Olympic Games which has been met with mixed reactions. You have been asked to write a short article for your local English-language newspaper defending the bid. Your article should cover the following points:

1 why the city would make a good venue
2 the construction work that would be necessary
3 the disruption to normal lives during the games
4 conclusion: the long-term and short-term benefits for the city

4 **Look at the sentences below. Which point in the task in Exercise 3 could they be used to support?**

a All in all, I think we should welcome the chance to host the games ... ☐

b Curiously, there has been some hostility towards the city's bid to host the Olympics ... ☐

c Although it will entail some upheaval in the short term ... ☐

d However, the long-term benefits far outweigh the short term disruption ... ☐

e In addition, we will need to upgrade the present infrastructure as well as ... ☐

f There will inevitably be some disruption to everyday lives. However, ... ☐

g New roads will obviously be needed, as will ... ☐

h ... and in addition it is perfectly located ... ☐

5 **Make brief notes on your ideas under the four headings.**

1 why the city would make a good venue

____
____
____
____
____

2 the construction work that would be necessary

____
____
____
____
____

3 the disruption to normal lives during the games

____
____
____
____
____

4 conclusion: the long-term and short-term benefits for the city

____
____
____
____
____

6 **Write your article using your notes and the useful expressions from Exercises 1 and 4. You should write approximately 250 words.**

4 Story

GRAMMAR

1 Underline the correct alternative.

a We were on the point of leaving / to leave when they finally arrived.

b I was just about **to send** / **sending** the email when I noticed I'd clicked "Reply all."

c The president was **have opened** / **to have opened** the gallery, but a security alert meant the honors were done by the vice president on his behalf.

d I'd been thinking **to drive** / **of driving** to San Francisco, but I took the train instead.

e Hernández was on the verge **of signing** / **to sign** with the Red Sox, but an eleventh-hour bid from the Yankees was too lucrative to resist.

f Play was **resuming** / **to resume** at 1:30 p.m., but at twenty past, the heavens opened yet again.

2 Rewrite the sentences using the words in parentheses so the meanings are similar.

a We intended to leave way before dark, but we completely lost track of time. (going)

We *were going to leave way before dark*, but we completely lost track of time.

b Susan had almost given up hope when the doorbell rang. (verge)

Susan ______________________ when the doorbell rang.

c We wanted to set off by 5:30 p.m., but it was closer to 6:30 p.m. by the time we finally left. (hoping)

We ______________________, but it was closer to 6:30 p.m. by the time we finally left.

d I was not intending to tell him about Jack, but he insisted on hearing the whole story. (going)

I ______________________, but he insisted on hearing the whole story.

e It was originally planned that the attack would take place at nightfall, but there were last-minute concerns. (was to)

The attack ______________________ ________, but there were last-minute concerns.

f Sam was on the point of revealing everything when Helena came into the room. (just about)

Sam ______________________ ________ when Helena came into the room.

g My parents were a little disappointed in my choice of career. I always feared this. (would)

I always feared ______________________ ______________ in my choice of career.

h I had planned to pay her a visit, but she had gone to her sister's for the day. (going)

I ______________________, but she had gone to her sister's for the day.

3 Complete the sentences about events or situations in your life.

a I was once going to ______________, but ______________________

b The other day, I was just about to ______________ ______________________ when ______________________

c I always knew I'd ______________________ ______________________ ______________________ d I never thought I'd ______________________________

____

____

4 Match the discourse markers that have similar meanings.

a for example — 1 in addition
b too — 2 say
c strictly speaking — 3 by contrast
d that is to say — 4 particularly
e in particular — 5 in other words
f including — 6 likewise
g similarly — 7 such as
h on the other hand — 8 to be accurate

a	b	c	d	e	f	g	h
2							

5 Complete the sentences (a–g) with the discourse markers in the two boxes.

likewise ~~particularly~~ such as to be accurate too

a I love reading autobiographies, particulary those of historical figures.

b I really love books that keep you guessing right up to the end. ______________, stories that have a sudden and totally unexpected ending.

c I really like some children's books, ______________ the Harry Potter series. And I like the books about the young James Bond, ______________.

d All seven Harry Potter books have been made into movies. ______________, there are actually eight movies, since the final book is made as two separate movies.

on the other hand or even strictly speaking that is to say

e I sometimes download movies from the internet. ______________, it's illegal, but everyone does it, don't they?

f I love all the old classic black and white movies of the 40s and 50s, ______________ the old silent movies from the 20s if I'm in the mood.

g The beach locations, ______________, 90% of the movie's scenes, looked amazing. The acting, ______________, left a lot to be desired.

6 Think of a book or a movie you know. Complete the sentences about this book or movie.

a It has some really funny parts, such as when Jack, the main character, forgets who he is.

b The main character is ______________________________

____

He / She ______________________________, too.

c I like ______________________________.
On the other hand, ______________________________

______________________________.

VOCABULARY

1 Complete the conversations with the expressions in the box.

cock-and-bull story ~~it's a long story~~ old wives' tale sob story tattle-tale the story of my life to cut a long story short

a A: So why did Jackie and Peter break up?
B: Oh, it's a long story. I'll tell you about it another time.

b A: Mommy, Evie drew on the wall at school today. But she said it was Jara who did it.
B: Don't be a ______________, Lauren. I'm sure the teacher knows all about it.

c A: Carlo says he was late this morning because his car wouldn't start.
B: Huh! That's a ______________ if ever I heard one. He only lives ten minutes away.

d A: You're not going to believe this! Five of my lottery numbers came up this week. But, guess what – it was the one week I didn't buy a ticket. It's ______________.
B: Oh well, five numbers wouldn't have won that much anyway.

e A: Mel and Joe broke up. Mel's really upset.
B: Oh, she'll be OK in a day or two. She always has some ______________ about how her boyfriends keep leaving her.

f A: How did you get that black eye?
B: Well, ______________, Alexandra hit me.

g A: Is it true that eating hot, spicy food makes you bad-tempered?
B: No, it's just an ______________.

2 Complete these literary extracts with the adjectives in the box.

astute fishy gullible plausible skeptical ~~unfaithful~~ unscrupulous

a She was struck by the idea that maybe she was being foolish in remaining faithful to her husband while Joe was so obviously unfaithful to her.

b Kate felt inordinately pleased at his offer, even though she was ______________ enough to know that it came from a desire for any company, rather than hers specifically.

c "And you believed me?" she asked, shaking her head in disbelief.
"Give me a break! Of course I didn't. I'm not that ______________," came Jim's reply.

d So he had given Katherine a call and asked if she would give him some advice on the matter. It seemed a reasonably ______________ excuse for inviting her to spend more time with him.

e "You're completely ______________, Linda," said Betty. "You should be ashamed. Illegal is one thing, but immoral is another."

f Molly gave a ______________ shrug. "I'm really not so sure about Nicola's story. Sounds like just the kind of thing she would have made up to impress Harry."

g There was something ______________ about the whole setup. He tried to think himself into a detective frame of mind. What would Sherlock Holmes do in the circumstances?

3 Match the adjectives (a–g) from Exercise 2 with words (1–7) with similar meaning.

1 cynical [f]
2 naive [ ]
3 dubious [ ]
4 dishonest [ ]
5 credible [ ]
6 streetwise [ ]
7 disloyal [ ]

4 Here are some ways of responding to a story or something you hear. Match the beginnings (a–g) with the endings (1–7).

a	Oh, no. What a	1	wow!
b	I'm not	2	you!
c	What a	3	relief!
d	I don't	4	awful!
e	Lucky	5	surprised!
f	How	6	nightmare!
g	Oh,	7	blame you!

a	b	c	d	e	f	g
6						

5 Write appropriate responses, using five of the expressions from Exercise 4. More than one expression is appropriate in some cases.

a A: Tom's house was broken into last night. I think they took a lot.
B: How awful!

b A: Sarah borrowed my camera and left it on the bus. I'm absolutely furious with her.
B: ______________________! I would be, too.

c A: How was the flight?
B: Don't ask! There was a last-minute delay and we spent six hours in the departure lounge.
A: ______________________!

d A: Hey, guess who won $1,000 in the lottery last night?
B: ______________________!

e A: It's OK. They found him safe and well.
B: Whew! ______________________!

PRONUNCIATION

1 11 Listen to the same sentence said with the main stress in two different places. Check (✓) the sentence in which things happened as planned, and put a cross (✗) next to the sentence in which things didn't happen as planned.

a I was planning to arrive at six. [ ]
b I was planning to arrive at six. [ ]

2 12 Listen to the pairs of sentences and put a check (✓) or cross (✗) according to whether things happened as expected or not.

a i We were planning to surprise her. [ ]
ii We were planning to surprise her. [ ]

b i I was hoping we'd be having pizza. [ ]
ii I was hoping we'd be having pizza. [ ]

c i We expected him to get an A. [ ]
ii We expected him to get an A. [ ]

d i You were supposed to dress up. [ ]
ii You were supposed to dress up. [ ]

e i The plane was due to arrive at 3:30 p.m. [ ]
ii The plane was due to arrive at 3:30 p.m. [ ]

f i I thought he'd be late. [ ]
ii I thought he'd be late. [ ]

Listen again and repeat.

LISTENING

1 ▶ 13 **Cover the listening script on the right and listen to a short story adapted from *The Gift of the Magi* by the American author O. Henry. Answer the questions.**

a Who are the two main characters?

____

b What is the relationship between them?

____

c What are their most prized possessions?

____

____

d What Christmas gifts did they buy for each other?

____

____

2 **Listen again. Number the events below in the order they are mentioned in the story.**

a Della remembered how she and Jim saw some combs in a store window. ☐
b Jim sold his watch. ☐
c Della decided to sell her hair. 1
d Della bought a gold watch chain for Jim. ☐
e Jim came home from work that evening. ☐
f Della gave Jim his gift. ☐
g Jim opened his gift. ☐
h Jim gave Della her gift. ☐
i Della opened her gift. ☐

Did the events take place in the same order as they are described in the story?

3 **Read the story and find words or phrases that mean:**

a collect or gather ______________
b dark red ______________
c put on carelessly ______________
d walked determinedly ______________
e a piece of hair ______________
f valued greatly ______________
g gave ______________
h a quick look ______________
i shaking nervously ______________
j moved clumsily ______________

The Christmas Gifts

Della so wanted to get her husband Jim something special for Christmas, but the few cents she'd managed to scrape together weren't going to go very far.

As she stood in front of the mirror, her beautiful, long auburn hair hanging over her shoulders, she had an idea. She flung on her coat and marched out onto the street. She stopped in front of a door which bore a sign saying "Hair Goods of All Kinds." She pushed the door open and walked in.

"Will you buy my hair?" asked Della. "Twenty dollars. Will that do you?" said the old lady. Della nodded, fighting back the tears as the first lock fell to the floor. But once she had the money in her hand, the smile returned to her face.

She knew exactly what she was looking for. The one possession that Jim prized above all others was a gold pocket watch that had been his father's and his grandfather's before him, but it had no chain. And Della wanted to buy him a simple gold chain to hold this precious watch. She handed over the twenty dollars, wrapped the chain up safely and set off for home.

On her way, she stopped to look in the window of her favorite store. It sold antique knick-knacks and there in the window lay a set of beautiful hair combs. She and Jim had stopped here the other day to admire them. He told her that the combs would have looked beautiful against the dark red of her hair. Della caught a glimpse of her reflection in the window. What would Jim say? She was sure he'd forgive her once he saw his gift. And anyway, she thought her hair looked OK in its new, boyish style.

That evening she felt excited, and when she heard Jim's footsteps, she ran to the door. The look on his face when he saw her was a hundred times worse than anything she could have expected. His face crumpled and he reached out his hand, saying "Your hair."

She ran towards him, crying and apologizing, "Jim, I'm sorry, I sold it to buy you a gift. Look!" and she thrust the tiny package in his hand. He, at the same time, reached into his pocket and held out a small package of about the same size.

"My darling, of course I love you, with or without your hair, it's just that I bought these for you ..."

They both took the small, simply wrapped gifts from each other's trembling hands. Della opened hers. There in her hand lay the combs.

"Oh, my love," she whispered, "They're beautiful, but don't worry, my hair'll grow. Go ahead, open your gift ..."

His hands fumbled on the paper as he pulled out the gold chain, and his mouth shaped itself into a sad smile. "Don't you like it?" she asked anxiously. "It's perfect," he said. "But it's just that ... I sold my watch this evening ... to buy the combs!"

5 Bargain

GRAMMAR

1 Underline the correct alternative in these news stories.

FLOWER POWER

A florist in Chicago is offering bunches of dead roses wrapped in black paper for jilted lovers to send to their exes. The owner says the inspiration for the idea was her boyfriend, **she split up with last month / whom she split up with last month**.

SECURITY RISK

A shoplifter was given a six-week jail sentence by a court in Nebraska yesterday after he removed a security tag from an item of clothing and tried to walk out of the store with it so it couldn't be used as evidence. "It's not something **I'm proud of / of I'm proud**," Paul Gracia, 26, said as he left the court. It is the fifth shoplifting offense **of which Gracia has been convicted / which Gracia has been convicted**.

COUNTING ON THE MONEY

A woman from Michigan, **whom Dracula and vampires have been a life-long obsession for / for whom Dracula and vampires have been a life-long obsession**, has set up a company which imports and sells coffins from Transylvania. The company sells five different products, **the most popular of which is painted blood red / of the most popular which is painted blood red**.

HITTING THE JACKPOT

A man **whom the local golf club was a second home for / for whom the local golf club was a second home**, and who bought his wife a lottery ticket only to stop her complaining, has won the $500,000 jackpot. And what is the lucky Mr. Stein going to treat himself to first? "There's a new set of clubs **for I've been saving up / I've been saving up for**," he said.

2 **Rewrite the sentences to make them more formal or informal.**

a This is the store from which I got my camera.
This is the store I got my camera from.

b Is this the hotel in which we stayed last year?
____

c Jo is someone you can always rely on.
____

d It's technically a crime, but nothing you'd be arrested for.
____

e The person to whom you need to speak is not here right now.
____

f Are they the people Scott went on vacation with?
____

3 **Which of the twelve sentences in Exercise 2 are formal (*F*) and which are informal (*I*)?**

4 **Rewrite the sentences as one sentence using a non-defining relative clause.**

a He earns about $200 a week. He spends most of it on computer games.
He earns about $ 200 a week, most of which he spends on computer games.

b I have a few friends in California. Most of them live in Los Angeles.
____

c We made a lot of food for the party. Most of it didn't get eaten.
____

d There are eight Ivy League colleges in the USA. The oldest is Harvard.
____

e We have exams all next week. The first exam is math.
____

5 **Underline the two correct alternatives in the each sentence.**

a I'm going to the **work** / **office** / **bed** / **mall**.

b William's not here. He's at **store** / **gym** / **home** / **school**.

c I'm going to **theater** / **work** / **school** / **gym** later.

d Let's meet outside **library** / **Tom's house** / **Café Coco** / **café** at 7:30 p.m.

e Alex is at the **café** / **bed** / **home** / **movies**.

f I'd like to work for the **police** / **education** / **medicine** / **government**.

g I don't like the **Brahms's music** / **music of Brahms** / **Brahms's 4th Symphony** / **Brahms you were playing last night**.

h When did you leave **party** / **home** / **school** / **mall**?

i I've always loved the **paella** / **paella for lunch** / **paella in this restaurant** / **paella my mother makes**.

6 **Fill in the blanks with *a/an*, *the*, or – (no article).**

a I live in _the_ south of Brazil, in a small town _____ south of Porto Alegre.

b We usually have _____ lunch at home, but we're going out for _____ surprise birthday lunch for my mom today.

c I hardly ever go anywhere by _____ bus. In fact, I last went on _____ bus about a year ago.

d We put off the party until _____ next weekend because that's _____ weekend my brother and his family are visiting us.

e I buy things on _____ internet all the time. I think _____ internet shopping is fantastic.

f I hope that one day we have _____ world without crime or violence or wars. One day we might have _____ world peace.

g People say _____ French often criticize foreigners who don't speak _____ French, but I have never found that to be true.

PRONUNCIATION

Look at the sentences below. Decide whether *the* is usually pronounced as /ðə/ or /ði/.

a The TV remote control is on the table.

b Is the umbrella in the hallway?

c This is the oldest building in the city.

d Don't use the printer. The ink's running out.

e The ice rink is next to the park. Just before the college building.

f The exam's on the 8th. In the afternoon.

g The movie was great. The scene at the end was amazing.

▶ 14 **Listen and check. Repeat the sentences.**

VOCABULARY

1 **Combine words in Box A with those in Box B to make expressions connected with money. Then use these expressions to complete the sentences.**

A

down	fancy	impulse	~~make~~	shop

B

around	buy	~~do~~	meal	payment

a I can't afford a new pair of jeans. I'll have to _make do_ with these old ones for a while longer.

b It's always a good idea to _____________ and compare prices before you buy anything.

c I've never even worn this pink and orange shirt. It was an _____________ last summer. I thought it looked cool at the time.

d Hey, let's celebrate the end of the year with a _____________ at that new restaurant.

e If you can't afford to pay in full, you can always make a _____________ of, say, 10% to reserve the item.

2 **Write true answers to the questions.**

a Have you ever overspent on something? What was it?

____

b When did you last have a fancy dinner?

____

c Do you generally live within your means?

____

d Name something that in your opinion is generally overpriced.

____

e Name something that in your opinion is exorbitantly priced.

____

f Have you ever made an impulse buy? What was it?

____

3 **Look at this extract from a radio show and complete what Steve says with the correct form of the phrasal verbs in the box.**

come through	cut back	get around	get by
~~get into~~	live on	pay off	run up
save up	splash out		

Interviewer: As part of our feature on student life, we're talking about money. With me first off today is Steve, who just graduated from college. So, Steve, how is it being a student these days, financially speaking?

Steve: Well, it's not great. I mean, if your parents can't afford it, you (1) __get into__ debt before you've even started. You can get a part-time job, but it really isn't enough to (2) __________ , so you have to use credit cards and maybe even borrow from other relatives and take out loans. So most students have (3) __________ even more debts by the time they graduate.

Interviewer: And was that the case for you?

Steve: Well, I started off spending without thinking, you know, (4) __________ on this and that. But I soon realized that I was going to have to (5) __________ on much, much less each week. Also, I originally thought I'd be able to (6) __________ to go away during summer vacation, but that was never going to happen.

Interviewer: So, what did you do to start economizing?

Steve: I started (7) __________ on what I spent by, say, buying supermarket brands, buying things in bulk, not going out so much, and that kind of thing. And I brought my old bike from home so I could (8) __________ without using public transportation.

Interviewer: And how did you do?

Steve: Well, I just about managed, although I have to say that my parents (9) __________ occasionally with financial help. My college days were fantastic, but it was hard having no money. I'm working full-time now, but I'm still (10) __________ my credit cards.

▶ 15 **Listen and check.**

4 **Complete the expressions using the words in the box.**

cost	frills	off	robbery	the red

a My account is always in __________ . I keep getting overdraft fees for being overdrawn.

b All these low-__________ , no-__________ airlines are pretty inexpensive, but the service is pretty bad, too, in my experience.

c Fifty dollars for that! What a rip-__________ ! It's not worth twenty. It's daylight __________ .

5 **Complete the conversations by choosing the best alternative.**

a A: I'm always __broke__ these days.
B: Get a new job. Or start spending less.
~~broke~~ / thrifty / frugal

b A: There are some great bargains in that clothing store on Market Street. Most things are __________ by at least 50%.
B: Great. I'll try and get there later.
short of money / affordable / discounted

c A: How was Suzy and Brad's wedding?
B: Amazing - incredibly __________ . I hate to think how much it cost.
exorbitant / lavish / generous

d A: What's that new restaurant like?
B: Not bad. And pretty __________ , too.
discounted / budget / affordable

e A: Should we try that new restaurant tonight?
B: I hear it's a little __________ . Maybe we should save it for a special occasion.
overpriced / affordable / no-frills

f A: It cost $300 to fix my computer.
B: How much? That's __________ . It should've been a hundred at the absolute most.
lavish / upscale / exorbitant

g A: How can you travel abroad for so long on so little money?
B: You have to be __________ - cheap hotels, get the bus instead of the train, and eat cheaply.
frugal / affordable / lavish

WRITING

Writing a news story
Features of a news story
Paragraph organization

- **You are going to write a news story called "New life for local couple." Follow these instructions.**

  a Read the notes below and make sure you have a clear picture of the story.

  b Decide which of the following is the most suitable paragraph for summarizing the story.

  (i) Dreams have come true for a local couple who inherited a farm and a family to go with it.

  (ii) Jennifer and Tyler Shaw start their dream business after inheriting a farm. Their plan to give underprivileged kids a taste of nature has brought them far more than they expected.

  (iii) Jennifer and Tyler Shaw's discovery of a time capsule has given them the chance to make their dreams come true. They hope to welcome hundreds of underprivileged children to their Friendly Farm.

  c Decide on a suitable order for the following paragraphs.

  - Jennifer's feeling about their new family ☐
  - The business idea and how it came about ☐
  - A brief summary of the story ☐
  - Details of their discovery ☐
  - The couple's plans for the future ☐
  - Background information about Jennifer and Tyler ☐
  - The consequences of their discovery ☐

  d Plan the contents of the paragraphs for your news story. Think about how to expand the notes into complete sentences and how to connect the sentences. You can use one of the summary paragraphs above if you like.

  e Write your news story. You should write approximately 250 words.

New life for local couple

Jennifer Shaw, happily married 15 years to Tyler, unable to have children

Receives letter, inherits old farm and money in uncle's will

Both love children, decide to create Friendly Farm for underprivileged children to experience farm life

While digging in backyard, find buried time capsule from 1975

Time capsule contents include newspapers, celebrity magazines, family pictures, and a personal diary

Research names through ancestry website and national records, find more than 15 cousins with 40 children

Hold family reunion at farm: "We are so happy to be part of this big, wonderful family. It's a dream come true."

Farm opens doors for underprivileged children, great success

Jennifer: "Next year we plan to open a family adventure course, and we already know who our first guests will be."

6 Mind

GRAMMAR

1 Some of these sentences have mistakes in them. Check (✓) the correct sentences and correct the ones that are wrong.

a What do you feel like doing? ~~I'm feeling~~ like going to the movies. I feel

b I'm not feeling well today. I think it must be the change in the weather. ______________

c If you'd been hearing the instructions, you'd know what to do. ______________

d He was hearing strange noises coming from the basement, so he grabbed a flashlight and climbed down to investigate. ______________

e I've been hearing a lot from Dylan recently. He emails me every day. ______________

f I think I'm smelling something burning. Are you sure you turned the oven off? ______________

g I'm just tasting the sauce. I think it needs more cheese. ______________

h This fish is tasting funny. Are you sure it's OK to eat? ______________

2 Underline the correct verb form(s). Both may be possible.

a **I'm hearing** / **can hear** a noise outside. Can you see if it's the cat?

b She **couldn't taste** / **didn't taste** the salt, so she decided to add a little more.

c I **can smell** / **'m smelling** the milk to see if it is fresh.

d He wasn't **hearing** / **able to hear** the song that clearly because of the noise in the background.

e I **could actually see** / **was actually seeing** my breath yesterday. I'm sure the temperature had dropped.

f As soon as they walked into the room they **could smell** / **were smelling** gas.

g Is the window open? I **can feel** / **'m feeling** a draft from somewhere.

h I **can sense** / **'m sensing** some resistance from you. Aren't you happy with the idea?

3 Complete the sentences with an appropriate verb of the senses. You may also need to use *can*, *could*, or *be able to*.

a I love listening to music when I'm working. It really helps me concentrate.

b I ______________ the noise of the traffic from my bed, but it doesn't stop me from sleeping.

c You ______________ the tension in the air whenever the boss is around.

d I ______________ particularly energetic today. I don't know why!

e I ______________ perfectly until the age of 30, then my eyesight started to deteriorate quickly.

f I don't like strong perfumes. I think they ______________ too chemical and unnatural.

Are these sentences true for you? If not, rewrite them so that they are.

4 Read the text below and underline the most appropriate participle clause.

Pushy Passengers Win Airline Dispute

Fifty-four airline passengers, (1) **spending** / **having spent** / **spent** three hours waiting at La Guardia Airport, were finally informed that their flight had been canceled due to technical problems. On (2) **hearing** / **having heard** / **heard** the news, one of the older passengers marched up to the airline office, (3) **demanding** / **having demanded** / **demanded** that they all be put on the next possible flight. However, (4) **overbooking** / **having overbooked** / **overbooked** the next flight, there was very little the airline could do.

The passengers all crowded around the airline desk, (5) **shouting and protesting** / **having shouted and protested** / **shouted and protested**. They threatened to block access to the other passengers trying to reach the check-in desks. Finally, (6) **wanted** / **having wanted** / **wanting** to do something to appease the angry crowd, the airline offered all the passengers free flights to the destination of their choice. (7) **Appeasing** / **Having appeased** / **Appeased** by this offer, they calmed down, took their seats, and waited another three hours before they finally took off, more than six hours late.

16 **Listen and check.**

5 **Rewrite each sentence using a participle clause.**

a He hadn't really understood what she'd said, so he did the exercise incorrectly.

Not having understood what she'd said, he did the exercise incorrectly.

b He's American, so he finds it hard to follow them when they start speaking Spanish.

____

c We worked really hard at the meeting, so we all went out for dinner on the company.

____

d He doesn't know the neighborhood very well, so there's a danger he'll get lost.

____

e He was cleared of theft by the court and immediately got his old job back.

____

VOCABULARY

1 **Rearrange the letters to make verbs associated with seeing. Use the clues to help you.**

a zega look thoughtfully for a long time

gaze

b menixae look closely or analytically

____

c conrigeze understand what or who you can see

____

d ratd your eyes do this when they move around quickly

____

e rbeosve watch or notice

____

f cnas look over something quickly

____

2 **Underline the correct alternative.**

a The doctor **gazed** / **examined** / **observed** the X-ray very carefully before speaking.

b He panicked, his eyes **darting** / **gazing** / **scanning** from side to side, looking for a way out.

c He looked at me for a long time and then shook his head. He really didn't seem to **scan** / **examine** / **recognize** me.

d She stood back and **gazed** / **observed** / **scanned** the scene in the room, happy not to be part of it for the moment.

e He **scanned** / **observed** / **recognized** the newspaper, looking for the article they'd just mentioned.

f She **examined** / **gazed** / **darted** out of the window at the pouring rain, thinking of anything but the class going on around her.

3 **Replace a word in each sentence with *observe*, *see*, or *recognize*.**

a I ~~admit~~ that it's not an easy language to learn.

recognize

b He doesn't really understand what you are trying to say.

____

c Writing in *The Times*, Steadman wrote that Smart's latest novel was a great disappointment.

____

d They have finally acknowledged his effort in the peacekeeping process.

____

e "You don't seem to be taking your studies very seriously," remarked the teacher.

____

f She said she was thinking of meeting Massimo later that evening.

____

g In our family we like to follow all the old New Year traditions.

____

h The state has realized that they need to put more funding into education.

____

4 **Complete the sentences with the words in the box.**

quizzical	slumped	leash	
sprang	tilting	barks	~~ramifications~~

a You ought to think about the *ramifications* before you make a decision.

b The Leaning Tower of Pisa is famous for _______________ precariously to one side.

c When I told Greg that I had changed my mind about the party, he gave me a _______________ look and shook his head.

d Sam's dog _______________ anytime someone even walks in front of the house. The neighbors are fed up.

e When we asked for volunteers, ten hands immediately _______________ up.

f Mrs. Robinson keeps her children on a short _______________. She has to; they are a wild bunch!

g My father _______________ down into the couch and turned on the TV. It had been a long day.

5 **Complete these expressions with *mind* using the words in the box.**

alike	~~up~~	off	on	out
over	own	two		

a make __up__ your mind
b mind your _______ business
c I'm of _______ minds
d take your mind _______ something
e go _______ of your mind
f Great minds think _______ .
g mind _______ matter
h the last thing _______ my mind

6 **Complete the sentences with the expressions in Exercise 5. Make any changes that are necessary.**

a Vacations? You want to plan a vacation? I'm sorry, that really is __the last thing on my mind__ right now.

b I don't mean to sound rude, but you know, she really does ask too many personal questions. I wish she'd learn to _______________ .

c I'm _______________ about this job offer. I really don't know what to do. They want an answer today but I need more time to think.

d Come on, we can do it. Let's give it one more try. Jon, you take that side, I'll take this one. And remember, it's a question of _______________ !

e _______________ ! I'm tired of waiting for you to choose.

f Hey! Is that your new cell phone? I have exactly the same one. Well, you know what they say, _______________ .

g Where have you been? Do you know what time it is? I was _______________ with worry!

h Come on! Let's go away for a couple of days. It'll help you _______________ things.

7 **Write the words in the correct order to form questions.**

a tomorrow leave Is I until it this if OK ?
__Is it OK if I leave this until tomorrow?__

b please that, repeating mind you Would ?
____

c husband May me bring I my with ?
____

d mind volume turning Would a little you the down ?
____

e please swap with seats Can you, I ?
____

8 **Match the requests (a–e) in Exercise 7 with these responses (1–5).**

1 I'm sorry, but I need to sit at the end of the row.
2 I'd really prefer it if you could do it today.
3 Why don't you just move a little farther away? This *is* a public place, you know.
4 Why? I think I made my message very clear.
5 Of course. He's very welcome.

a	b	c	d	e
2				

17 **Listen and check.**

PRONUNCIATION

1 **Write the noun form of the verbs and adjectives below.**

a stimulate __stimulation__
b observe _______________
c recognize _______________
d active _______________
e regular _______________
f creative _______________
g popular _______________
h perfect _______________
i familiar _______________
j anxious _______________

2 **Mark the stress on all the words in Exercise 1.**

18 **Listen and check. Notice how the stress changes in the nouns.**

LISTENING

1 19 **Cover the listening script on the right and listen to three people talking about stress. Make notes on the following questions.**

a What is the cause of their stress?

Mark: ______________________

Kay: ______________________

Liza: ______________________

b How does it affect them?

Mark: ______________________

Kay: ______________________

Liza: ______________________

c Make a note of two things they each do to counter the stress.

Mark: ______________________

Kay: ______________________

Liza: ______________________

2 Listen again. Which of the three people, Mark (*M*), Kay (*K*), or Liza (*L*):

a suffers from the emotional effects of stress? ☐
b finds that noise can be a source of stress? ☐
c suffers from the physical effects of stress? ☐
d doesn't like spending free time talking about work? ☐
e combats stress with physical activities? ☐
f feels the need to do something intellectually challenging? ☐
g combats stress with social activities? ☐
h combats stress with domestic activities? ☐

3 Find words or phrases in the listening script that mean:

a to relax (Mark / Kay) ______________
b unable to sit still because they're nervous or bored (Mark) ______________
c escape (Mark) ______________
d held back, shut in (Mark) ______________
e so boring it makes you depressed (Kay) ______________
f without energy (Kay) ______________
g to lie or sit with knees pulled up so as to make yourself comfortable (Kay) ______________
h becoming soft and liquid (Liza) ______________

Mark Well, I guess my job is pretty stressful. All medical professionals have pretty stressful jobs, but working in the ER is particularly bad. We have to be ready to react quickly and efficiently, and often people's lives are at stake. Sometimes, it can be really exhilarating, but it's also exhausting, both mentally and physically. I find it really difficult to unwind when I go home; I mean, I can't just go home and sit and watch TV, or read a book ... I'm too tense and get really fidgety. Some people find it's good to talk about their work - you know, go for a beer after work and all that, but I don't. I prefer to get away from it, play sports, maybe go running, go to the gym, or play a game of squash. Squash is really good. You can thrash out all the pent-up stress and release all that tension, and I find it really helps me just empty my mind and switch off.

Kay I live about sixty kilometers from where I work, and I commute in and out every day on a really busy commuter train. Sometimes there's nowhere to sit down, and you have to stand up all the way. I find it really stressful. There are cell phones ringing all the time and people listening to their music, and the sight of all those bored, gray faces is really soul-destroying. After a long day at work, I get home feeling totally drained and it often gives me a headache. I usually run a hot bath, play some soft music, and curl up with a good book for an hour or so, and that really helps. That and cooking - I find that all the preparation involved really helps me unwind.

Liza I've got two boys. One just turned two and the other's nine months old. They're great kids, but sometimes they just totally exhaust me! They continually want attention, whether they're hungry or tired or just bored. And I know I'm really lucky because I can afford not to go to work, so I get to spend all day with them, and that a lot of mothers have to share their energy between work and being with the children, but sometimes I really miss adult company ... being around kids all day can make you feel pretty dumb ... I sometimes feel like my brain is turning to mush. Sometimes, when I'm really tired and stressed out, I just sit down and cry. When it gets that bad, I leave the kids with their grandmother and dedicate a day to my mind! Going to a movie or an art exhibition, reading the newspaper from front to back, or maybe just meeting a friend for a long lunch and some adult conversation.

7 Digital

GRAMMAR

1 **Combine the short sentences to make one complex sentence. Use the framework given below and write no more than three words in each blank.**

- Netbooks are inexpensive and light.
- Netbooks appeal to a wide audience.
- They appeal to business people who travel frequently.
- They appeal to kids and home users.
- They are looking for a small laptop.
- They want to be able to carry it from room to room.
- They also appeal to students.
- They have to carry heavy books around with them all day.
- They don't want the extra weight of a full-size laptop.

Inexpensive and (1) ________________ , netbooks appeal to a wide audience, from (2) ______________________________ travel frequently to kids (3) ________________ users looking (4) ________________ laptop which they (5) ________________ from room to room, to students who (6) ________________ heavy books around all day and (7) ________________ the extra weight of a full-size laptop.

- Speech recognition has reached an important point in its development.
- With speech recognition you can navigate your computer without a keyboard and mouse.
- You can also write documents without using the keyboard and mouse.
- It's much faster with speech recognition.

(8) __________________________ has reached the point where you can actually (9) ________________________________ and (10) __________________________ faster than (11) ________________ with a (12) __________ ________________ .

2 **Look again at the short sentences in the boxes in Exercise 1. Cross out all the words and expressions that are not used in the longer sentences.**

3 **Write the phrases in the correct order to complete the complex sentences.**

a The perfect computer would be one ...
/ and light / that is so small / can open out / it can fit comfortably in your pocket, / to give you / but at the same time / a full-size screen / .

The perfect computer would be one that is so small and light it can fit comfortably in your pocket, but at the same time can open out to give you a full-size screen.

b I think speech recognition could ...
/ with physical disabilities / do so many good things, / to access / quickly and easily / all the functions on their computer / such as help people / .

____
____
____
____

c I would love to have ...
/ that can park itself, / in the parking lot / by lining itself up / and doing / for me! / all that awkward maneuvering / a car / .

____
____
____
____

4 **Write complex sentences that are true for you. Use the sentence openings below and try to include as much information as possible.**

a The next electronic device I buy will be a ________
____
____
____

b My idea of the perfect vacation is ______________
____
____
____

5 **Look at each pair of sentences. Is the meaning similar (*S*) or different (*D*)?**

1 a We'll probably have to eat less meat and fish as the agricultural industry cuts back on its carbon footprint.

b It is likely we'll be eating less meat and fish as the agricultural industry cuts back on its carbon footprint. [S]

2 a We're bound to see someone we know at the party.

b We might see someone we know at the party. [ ]

3 a He could easily change his mind tomorrow when he sees how challenging the class is.

b He definitely won't be of the same opinion tomorrow when he sees how challenging the class is. [ ]

4 a Experts believe that it is highly likely that the present generation of children will have an average life expectancy of over 100 years.

b Experts believe that the present generation of children may possibly live to be over 100. [ ]

5 a It is highly unlikely that a cure will ever be found for the common cold.

b We'll probably never find a cure for the common cold. [ ]

6 **There are mistakes in four of the following sentences. Find the mistakes and correct them.**

a Sea levels are likely *to* rise by over a meter by the end of the 21st century.

b There may be more electric cars than traditional gasoline-fueled cars on our roads in as little as five years.

c In ten years, we could easily be using our body heat to recharge our cell phones.

d With new advances in nanotechnology, cancer and tumors will certainly almost become a thing of the past.

e Bicycle-sharing initiatives could easily become compulsory in many cities.

f Scientists are bound to discovering a cure for Alzheimer's disease by the end of the century.

g Human beings won't definitely ever be able to live to more than 120.

Look at the sentences again. Which predictions do you think are a) probable and b) highly unlikely?

7 **Complete the sentences with the expressions in the box so they reflect what you believe and feel about the future. Do not use any expression more than once.**

will almost certainly	definitely won't	probably won't	might	should
couldn't possibly	may possibly	is/are sure to	is/are unlikely to	

a My children's generation ________________ have an easier life.

b Advances in technology ________________ reverse the process of climate change.

c In ten years I ________________ working a seven-day week.

d Digital texts ________________ take the place of paper books.

e Water ________________ become more precious than oil.

f A viable alternative for fossil fuels ________________ be found in the next twenty years.

g My generation ________________ live to over 120 years old.

h I ________________ have to move abroad to find a job in the next few years.

VOCABULARY

1 **Complete the compound nouns. Use one word in each blank.**

a This revolutionary communication d*evice* will soon make cell phones a thing of the past.

b He lives in a really remote place. It's a real "not spot" – there's no wi-fi and no cellular c________________. You're totally cut off from the world up there!

c They have a very extensive data n________________ with information on all public transportation schedules across the country.

d The local bus companies have just introduced a new payment s________________ that allows you to use your cell phone credit to buy a ticket.

e The offices are wired up to a security system that sends a remote a________________ to the local police station.

f I wish people would send me a text when they can't get through on the cell phone. I hate having to check my v________________!

g New speech r________________ software will mean that you can talk to your computer, but only if you have an American accent!

h I find grocery s________________ such a drag. I hate waiting in line, and I always end up buying a ton of stuff I really don't need.

i Have you been to Tom's place? He has this amazing home-e________________ system with a flat screen that hooks up directly to his netbook and plays movies and music directly off the internet.

2 **Underline the correct word or expression.**

a The audience was really **hyped** / **wowed** by the special effects.

b Did you know that millions of cell phones are **slick** / **trashed** every year?

c There was a delay of over a year and a half before the TV channel finally **sold on the idea** / **went digital**.

d The presentation of the new prototype was very **slick** / **wow** and impressive.

e As soon as he saw the sales figures, he was completely **sold on the idea** / **trashed**!

f There was so much **hype** / **slick** when the movie first came out that it was very difficult for it to live up to expectations.

3 **Use words or expressions from Exercise 2 to complete the texts below.**

> There's no such thing as bad publicity, or so the saying goes, but sometimes too much (1) ________________ can backfire. Take a recent "revolutionary" invention which claimed in its pre-launch publicity that it would profoundly affect the way people lived. The speculation reached dizzying heights, and everybody was getting ready to be (2) ________________ by a must-have device which would change all our lives overnight. Imagine the disappointment when it turned out to be nothing more than a low-energy scooter!
>
> Do you know, that man could sell ice to Eskimos!

> His presentation was so (3) ________________ and clever. Not too overstated, not too loud or brash; he pitched it just right for his audience, and we were all totally (4) ________________ .
>
> I signed up right away!

> As more and more schools and colleges prepare to (5) ________________ , traditional textbook writers and publishers are worried. Is this the end of paper books? Will all those much thumbed, much loved textbooks now just be (6) ________________ ? Will we all convert to e-textbooks brought to us on our cell phones and e-readers?

4 **Complete the sentences using one word in each blank.**

a What's all the soul-searching about? It's not such a big ___*deal*___, you know. And hey, if you make the wrong decision, you can always change your mind.

b Listen, I've thought it ____________ really carefully, and I've decided that the answer is going to have to be no. I'm sorry!

c Don't rush things; take your time. This is a really important decision, and remember, once you've made it, there's no going ____________ .

d Stop dwelling on it. There's nothing you can do to change the past. What's ____________ is ____________ . Forget it and move on.

e Now, I know I've asked you this before, but are you sure you've thought through all the ____________ consequences?

f It's no good, I just keep going ____________ and ____________ in circles. I'm never going to be able to make up my mind.

g Why don't you ____________ on it and let me know in the morning?

h Come on, what's with the long face? It isn't the ____________ of the world, is it?

20 **Listen and check.**

PRONUNCIATION

1 21 **Listen and underline the stressed part of the compound nouns in bold.**

a Can I borrow your **cell phone**?

b Where's the **remote control** for the TV?

c Have you taken a look at the **travel schedule** yet? It's a killer!

d It's a little cold. Do you mind if I turn up the **central heating**?

e I love these **touch screen** phones, but they're really difficult to keep clean.

f That's a really pretty **wristband**. Where did you get it?

2 22 **Listen again and repeat the sentences.**

WRITING

Writing a discursive essay
Writing an introduction
Using discourse markers

1 Which of the following things might you expect to see in the introduction to an essay?

- a An introduction to the topic, demonstrating why the topic area is worth considering
- b Some of your arguments
- c Your general opinion
- d A basic repetition of the question
- e Evidence to support your arguments
- f A preview of your conclusion
- g A list of detailed examples
- h An outline of what you plan to say

2 Read two introductions to two essays which are answering the same question. What is the question?

- a Who was the greatest inventor of the 20th century?
- b Which was the most important discovery of the last fifty years?
- c What do you consider to be the most important invention of modern times?

a

Nowadays, the internet plays a major role in many areas of our society. However, I don't think it is as important as the camera. When we started using the camera, we completely changed our way of recording the past. Nowadays, almost all families have digital cameras and camcorders – or use the same applications on their cell phones – and use them to record weddings, anniversaries, and special moments in their day-to-day lives. Before the camera, people had to record the past with paintings, and so that is why there are far fewer records of the period before the camera was invented.

b

Many people, looking back over the last part of the 20th century, claim that the internet has had a bigger impact on our lives than any other recent invention. I believe this to be a rather short-sighted view of our history. The car, the telephone, and the television have all played a significant role in shaping our society. But when it comes to helping us record our past, I strongly believe there is only one candidate, the camera.

3 Read the two introductions again and decide which one is the best. Use your answers to Exercise 1 to help you.

4 Complete the text with some of the discourse markers in the box.

as well as	but then	but with
for the first time	in this sense	
it also meant that	not only	prior to

(1) ________________ did the camera change the way we record history, (2) ________________ people from all walks of life could participate in creating historical documents for future generations.
(3) ________________ the invention of the camera, almost all visual recollections of the past were in the form of paintings and drawings, which tended to be commissioned by the nobility, or for religion. There were far fewer documents of how normal life was lived. (4) ________________ the introduction of the camera, this all changed. (5) ________________, people from all walks of life were able to document their lives.

5 Choose an invention and write three reasons why you think it is the greatest invention of modern times.

Invention ________________________________

Reasons why:

1 ________________________________

2 ________________________________

3 ________________________________

6 Write an essay which answers this question, using discourse markers from Exercise 4.

"What do you consider to be the most important invention of modern times?"

You should write approximately 250 words.

8 The law

GRAMMAR

1 Complete the second sentence so it has the same meaning as the first sentence.

a Katie Steams was listening to the radio in her kitchen when she heard that the radio station was giving away a free convertible.

In her kitchen, listening to the radio, Katie Steams heard that the radio station was giving away a free convertible.

b To win the convertible, you had to answer three simple questions.

What you had ______________________________

____

c Katie put down the potato she was peeling and called the radio station.

Putting ______________________________

____

d The DJ read the three questions, and Katie answered them correctly.

The three questions ______________________________

____

e When she went to the radio station to collect her prize, the DJ handed her a 10-centimeter model of a convertible.

What the DJ ______________________________

____

____

f Katie was furious and decided to sue the radio station.

Furious, ______________________________

____

g The judge ruled in her favor and ordered the radio station to pay Katie $40,000 for the real car.

Ruling ______________________________

____

2 Complete the conversation with appropriate modal verbs. Sometimes there is more than one possible answer.

Glen: Hi, Alan. You know that money I lent Larry? Well, he promised he (1) ___would___ pay me back within three weeks, but he (2) ____________ have forgotten.

Alan: Well, didn't I warn you not to trust him? You (3) ____________ have made him write you a check; then you (4) ____________ have avoided all these problems.

Glen: Well, you never know, he (5) ____________ have genuinely forgotten.

Alan: Well, I think it's more likely that it conveniently slipped his mind. Anyway, didn't he say he (6) ____________ come over to see us this weekend? Well, where is he?

Glen: Yes, you're right. I (7) ____________ have insisted that he give me a check.

23 **Listen and check.**

3 Each of the following sentences has one word missing. Insert the missing words.

a She promised she [would] call if there were any problems.

b I'm really sorry. I have been looking where I was going.

c I know I really ought have called sooner, but I was really busy.

d His phone was busy. I guess he might have talking to his sister.

e I thought he'd have arrived by now – he must gotten stuck in the traffic.

f Why are you still working? You should finished that report by now.

g You should have told me there was no food in the house – I have gone to the store.

h I'm sorry, I really don't know where it is – I guess might have left it at home.

4 **Rewrite the following sentences using the modal verb in parentheses.**

a He's over an hour late. The only possible explanation is that he forgot about the appointment. (must)

He's over an hour late. He must have forgotten about the appointment.

b "I really can't afford to buy a new car; it's way too expensive," he explained. (could)

____

c She believes it was possibly intentional. (might)

____

d I told you to get the furnace checked. Now it doesn't work, it's freezing, and it's the middle of the winter. (should)

____

e "I'll make sure all the doors are locked and all the lights turned off," Cathy promised. (would)

____

f They can't be the ones who stole the money because they didn't have enough time. (could)

____

5 **Match the beginnings of the sentences (a–g) with their endings (1–7).**

a He was so disappointed with the outcome of the court case
b She wasn't expecting to get the job
c He hates the fact that he has to work the night shift
d There was such confusion over the new voting system
e He has such a bad reputation for not paying his debts
f She wasn't happy to help
g They were so surprised when he told them that he'd passed his exam

1 that no one will lend him any money.
2 and his wife, who has to spend the evenings alone, does, too.
3 that they could hardly believe him.
4 and she wasn't willing to say why.
5 and she certainly didn't expect to be offered such a generous salary.
6 that he decided to give up practicing law.
7 that many people voted for the wrong candidate.

a	b	c	d	e	f	g
6						

VOCABULARY

1 **Choose the correct answer.**

a Which of these punishments would a judge probably not give in court?
1 jail sentence
2 solitary confinement
3 community service

b Which one of these crimes involves fire?
1 arson
2 embezzlement
3 speeding

c Which one of these is the least serious crime?
1 manslaughter
2 speeding
3 libel

d Which of these is a lawyer?
1 attorney
2 libel
3 the accused

e Which of the following does the judge not do?
1 award damages
2 cross-examine
3 sentence

f Which of the following does the jury not do?
1 return a verdict
2 weigh up the evidence
3 sue

2 **Use words and phrases from Exercise 1 to complete the sentences below.**

a When her company fired her with no warning or advance notice, Clare decided to *sue* them for damages.

b It was the worst case of ____________ that the fire department had ever seen.

c ____________ bowed her head and cried as the sentence against her was read in the courtroom.

d The judge sentenced the two teenage boys to eight months of ____________, stressing that he hoped that helping others would help them see the error of their ways.

e The counsel for the defense stood up to ____________ the witness, but said he had no questions to ask.

f The case was so straightforward, the jury took only 30 minutes to ____________ of guilty.

g It was the third time he'd been stopped for ____________ – and on the same stretch of road!

h The newspaper was cleared of all charges of ____________ on the grounds that the story they had previously reported had since been shown to be true.

3 **Complete these expressions to do with the law with the words in the box.**

above against by down into of ~~unto~~ with

a a law __unto__ himself
b lay ________ the law
c taking the law ________ your own hands
d no one is ________ the law
e in trouble ________ the law
f the long arm ________ the law
g ________ law
h ________ the law

4 **Choose the most appropriate expressions from Exercise 3 to complete the sentences below.**

a It's up to the police to control crime. There's no point in ________________________ .
b The police are always going to his parents' house. He's constantly ________________________ .
c Her father really used to ________________________ . He would order her to be home by 11:00 p.m.
d He acts like he's ________________________ and can get away with anything, but one day he'll find himself in big trouble.
e You can never tell how Tony's going to react. He's ________________________ .
f Playing music in the subway is prohibited ________________________ unless you have a license.
g It is ________________________ to drive a motorcycle without wearing a helmet.
h No matter where you hide, ________________________ will be able to reach you.

5 **Match the formal words (a–h) with their more neutral forms (1–8).**

a prior to
b prominent
c seek
d severe
e further
f depict
g commence
h in due course

1 start
2 very bad
3 in addition
4 before
5 well-known
6 later
7 ask for
8 show

a	b	c	d	e	f	g	h
4							

6 **Complete each exclamation with one word. The first letter has been given to you.**

a Did I h__ear__ you right? They're going to arrest him?
b Come on, you've g________ to be kidding! She'd never do anything like that!
c You don't e________ me to believe that, do you? I've never heard such nonsense in all my life!
d Well, I n________ ! Who'd have t________ it! She really is a dark horse, isn't she?
e Why not? You never can t________ . Dave's always known how to surprise us.

7 **Write the words in the correct order to form common idiomatic expressions associated with surprise and disbelief.**

a fly and might pigs
____
b book can't you cover judge by a its
____
c waters deep still run
____
d hurt fly a wouldn't
____

8 **Match the idioms (a–d) in Exercise 7 with their meanings (1–4).**

1 Used for saying that people who are shy or who do not say much often have very strong feelings or interesting ideas. ☐
2 Used for saying that you thought someone was a very gentle person and wouldn't do anything to injure or upset anybody. ☐
3 Used for saying you shouldn't form an opinion about someone or something only from their appearance. ☐
4 Used for saying that something is completely impossible. ☐

PRONUNCIATION

24 **Listen to these people expressing surprise. Look at the words in bold and think about whether the speaker's voice is high or low, and rising or falling.**

a **No**! You've got to be **kidding**!
b No **way**! He wouldn't hurt a **fly**!
c You did **what**? I can't **believe** it!
d **Who** did you say? **Mike**? That just **can't** be right.
e **Really**? The **two** of them? But **when**?
f Well, **who**'d have thought? What a **dark** horse!

Listen again and repeat.

LISTENING

1 ▶ 25 **Cover the listening script on the right and listen to two friends, Alan and Sarita, discussing the problems involved in having jury duty. Make a note of what they think is:**

a the main problem

____

____

b a possible benefit of having jury duty

____

____

2 **Listen again and decide if the statements below are true (T) or false (F).**

a Neither speaker has ever had jury duty. ☐
b They have both been reading the same article in the newspaper. ☐
c Some employers refuse to give their employees permission to have jury duty. ☐
d Jurors are paid their normal salary during jury duty. ☐
e Most people are happy to have jury duty. ☐
f Some court cases can last a long time. ☐
g Sometimes jurors are not allowed to see their families during jury duty. ☐
h Sarita is interested in having jury duty. ☐

3 **Complete each extract from the conversation with an appropriate preposition.**

a ... more and more people are trying to get _____ of it if they can.
b ... there's a problem about taking time _____.
c ... they don't actually have to pay your salary when you're _____ jury duty ...
d ... it's much less than most people earn _____ work ...
e I mean, it sounds like a good thing to do _____ theory ...
f ... but if you're going to be worse _____ ...
g ... that seems to be what's _____ the root of the problem.
h ... you might be called to sit _____ a simple case
i ... the jury has to be isolated _____ the press

Listen again and check.

Alan: Have you ever had jury duty?

Sarita: No, I haven't. Why are you asking?

Alan: Oh, nothing ... just that I've been reading in the paper about how more and more people are trying to get out of it if they can.

Sarita: Really? I think it'd be really interesting.

Alan: Yeah, so do I, but it seems that there's a problem about taking time off work.

Sarita: Yeah? What, like their bosses won't give them time off?

Alan: No, no, that's not the problem. I mean, your employer has to let you take time off. I mean, they can't refuse to give you the time off. No, no, sometimes they might actually be really happy to, you know, because they don't actually have to pay your salary when you're on jury duty.

Sarita: Are you sure? That seems very strange.

Alan: Well, I think it's true; that's what it says here, anyway.

Sarita: But if you're not being paid ... I mean, that's hardly very fair, is it?

Alan: I think you get some kind of allowance ... you know, you get, like, a daily allowance while you're on jury duty.

Sarita: That sounds more like it. I mean, they can't force you to do something without offering some compensation.

Alan: Yeah, but apparently it's not a lot ... I mean, it's much less than most people earn at work, so lots of jurors are doing everything they can to get out of doing their stint.

Sarita: Hmm, yeah, I see ... I think I would, too ... I mean, it sounds like a good thing to do in theory ... you know, interesting to find out exactly how our justice system works and all that, but if you're going to be worse off ... well ...

Alan: Yeah, that seems to be what's at the root of the problem. That, and the time it takes sometimes.

Sarita: What do you mean?

Alan: Well, you might be called to sit on a simple case which only takes a matter of days, but some cases can go on for weeks ... or months, even.

Sarita: Yeah, and what about if you get called onto some high-profile case ... you know, something that's in the news. The pressure must be really tough.

Alan: Yeah, the jury has to be isolated from the press ... sometimes they can't even speak to their own families.

Sarita: Well, in that case, I think I'd try to get out of it, too!

9 Night

GRAMMAR

1 Underline the correct alternative.

a The average adult needs about eight hours of sleep a night. Some studies, **however** / **yet** / **although**, suggest that women need an hour more sleep than men.

b Eating dinner just before bed is not recommended. Eating a small snack, **yet** / **though** / **although**, can actually help you sleep.

c Men tend to dream more about men, **however** / **but** / **even though** women, according to research, dream equally about men and women.

d We very often dream about ourselves, **despite** / **although** / **however** this doesn't start happening until we are about five years old.

e Sleepwalkers are technically asleep, **even so** / **even though** / **despite** they have their eyes open and sometimes even engage in conversation.

f Some animals, such as cows and elephants, can sleep standing up. They can only dream when they are lying down **yet** / **even so** / **though**.

g **Even though** / **Despite** / **However** many years of research, it is still not known whether fish sleep at all.

h Everyone knows the expression "thinking on your feet," **yet** / **although** / **even so** studies have shown that, on average, we think 10% faster when we are lying down.

2 Complete the news items with the words in the boxes.

but	despite	~~even though~~	though

CONSIDERATE CAR THIEF

Joe Davis of Miami is still furious, (1) *even though* the thief that rifled through his car and took his CDs, cash, driver's license, and credit cards left a nice note behind.

The note read: "*You have amazing taste in music. Don't worry about your credit cards and driver's license – I know I can't use them … after tonight, at least. Seriously* (2) ____________ *, lock your car in the future.*"

The note was handwritten and signed "P," but (3) ____________ the thief's audacity, his or her identity remains unknown.

Police say that a thief leaving a note is rare, (4) ____________ that car burglaries are not.

despite	even though	however	nevertheless	yet

FAKE PHONE FELONS

Employees at a cell phone store arrived at work on Tuesday morning to find that the store had been broken into. (5) ____________ , the only items missing were hollow replica display phones.

"(6) ____________ they look real, they are completely worthless," said store manager Eva Martinez. "We've got hundreds of real phones on the premises, (7) ____________ the thieves just walked right past them. It's a mystery."

(8) ____________ the minimal loss, the store owners (9) ____________ reported the theft to local police, who are investigating.

but	despite	however	saying that	try as I might

THE CRATE ESCAPE

John Franklin, a cleaner from Illinois, decided last month to mail himself to his best friend as a birthday surprise. He climbed into a large crate and got his wife to mail him to his friend's house thirty miles away. (10) ____________ , the crate got lost, and (11) ____________ Mr. Franklin's shouts and frantic banging, his plight was not discovered for six days. "(12) ____________ , I just couldn't get anyone's attention," said Franklin. Postal workers recalled hearing faint banging noises, (13) ____________ assumed it was the depot's heating system. Franklin's wife described her husband as "a raving lunatic." "(14) ____________ , I did get a six-day break from his incessant pranks," she added.

26 **Listen and check.**

3 Complete the sentences so that they are true for you.

a Try as I might, *I just can't stop eating chocolate.*

b Strange as it may seem, ________________________

c ________________________ . Saying that, ________________________

d In spite of my efforts, ________________________

e Try as I might, ________________________

4 **Complete these famous quotations about regret by putting the verbs into the correct tense or form.**

a I regret __not having had__ (not have) more time with my kids when they were growing up. (*Tina Turner, singer*)

b I wish I ________________ (invent) blue jeans. They have expression, modesty, sex appeal, simplicity – all I hope for in my clothes. (*Yves Saint Laurent, designer*)

c If I ________________ (know) I was going to live this long, I ________________ (take) better care of myself. (*Eubie Blake, musician*)

d I wish they ________________ (have) electric guitars in cotton fields back in the good old days. A whole lot of things ________________ (be) straightened out. (*Jimi Hendrix, musician*)

e I have no regrets. I ________________ (not live) my life the way I did if I ________________ (go) to worry about what people were going to say. (*Ingrid Bergman, actor*)

5 **Think of some regrets in your life. Write about them by completing the sentences below.**

a It's a real shame ________________________________

b I really regret ________________________________

c If only ________________________________

d I'd have liked ________________________________

PRONUNCIATION

1 ▶ 27 **In speech, *had*, *would*, and *have* are often contracted. Listen to how they are pronounced in these sentences.**

a I wish you had been there.

b If you had been there, you would have had a great time.

2 **How would the following sentences sound with *had*, *would*, and *have* contracted?**

a If only I had gone out last night.

b I wish I had had more time.

c If you had been there, you would have loved it.

d I would like to have gone with you.

e Peter would have loved it, too.

▶ 28 **Listen and check. Repeat the sentences.**

VOCABULARY

1 **Find nine times of day in the puzzle. One has been done for you. The words go →, ↓, and ↘.**

N	D	S	U	N	S	E	T	F
M	I	D	N	I	G	H	T	S
D	B	G	K	N	R	T	J	I
A	U	Y	H	S	O	Q	L	D
W	Z	S	H	T	P	O	H	O
N	B	X	K	Q	F	M	N	A
D	A	Y	B	R	E	A	K	Y
S	U	N	R	I	S	E	L	V
T	W	I	L	I	G	H	T	L

__sunrise__ ________________

________________ ________________

________________ ________________

________________ ________________

____

2 **Write the missing letters to complete these times of day.**

a th_e_ m_i_ddl_e_ _o_f th_e_ n_i_ght

b f_rst th_ng _n th_ m_rn_ng

c l_st th_ng _t n_ght

d th_ cr_ck _f d_wn

e m_d - _ft_rn_ _n

3 **Complete the sentences with the times of day in Exercise 2.**

a Sam called me from Australia in __the midle of the night__ last night. I think it was about 3:30 a.m. He'd forgotten about the time difference!

b I've been waking up at ________________ lately. I think it's the sun coming through the drapes that's waking me up.

c We'll try and set off around ________________ ________________. We'll have lunch and then pack, so I guess about four-ish.

d I like to read in bed for half an hour ________________ ________________. It helps me get to sleep.

e I'll call you ________________________________. What time do you get up?

4 Underline the correct alternative.

a It took me hours to **drop off** / **out** last night.

b I like a glass of water at the end of the day to help me **wind away** / **down**.

c I couldn't get to sleep last night. I was still **totally groggy** / **alert** at two in the morning.

d I was so tired last night I **slept like a tree** / **log**.

e I went out like a **light** / **night** last night.

f The neighbors were having an all-night party last night. I **didn't get a nod** / **wink of sleep**.

g I've always **been a light** / **gentle sleeper**. The slightest thing wakes me up.

h I need a few days' rest to **recharge my power** / **batteries**.

5 Match the expressions in bold in Exercise 4 with expressions with a similar meaning (1–8).

1 relax [b]
2 fall asleep [ ]
3 slept soundly [ ]
4 completely awake [ ]
5 had a sleepless night [ ]
6 fell asleep immediately [ ]
7 renew my energy levels [ ]
8 woken up easily when disturbed [ ]

6 Put the words in italics into the correct order in these conversations.

a A: Are you doing anything tonight?
B: *have No, what did mind? in you*
No, what did you have in mind?

b A: *to you What this evening? are up*
____
B: Nothing special.

c A: *drink you go a like 'd wondering I was if sometime? to for*
____
____
B: That sounds great! I'd love to!

d A: Want to come over for a bite to eat tonight?
B: *tonight. going but out you, really That's nice of I'm*
____
____

e A: Are you free on Thursday evening?
B: *have to do then. sorry. something I There's No, I*
____
____

f A: How about a game of tennis on Friday?
B: *Saturday. free make can't but I'm I Friday, on*
____
____

7 Complete the conversation with the words in the box.

felt	mind	neck	shame	sometime	sounds	time	~~up~~	up

Alex: Hi, Jim. It's Alex. What are you (1) __up__ to tonight?
Jim: I'm pretty busy, actually. I'm up to my (2) ______ in work right now.
Alex: Oh, that's a (3) ______ . I was wondering if you (4) ______ like going out for a drink.
Jim: I'd love to, but as I said, I'm really tied (5) ______ . Some other (6) ______ , maybe.
Alex: OK, never (7) ______ . Maybe (8) ______ next week?
Jim: Yeah, that (9) ______ good.

about	along	could	feels	good	make	say	then	to

Alex: How (10) ______ Monday? Or Tuesday?
Jim: Tuesday sounds (11) ______ . We (12) ______ check out that new bar on Eleventh Street.
Alex: OK. I hear it's pretty good. Eight thirty?
Jim: Actually, could we (13) ______ it a little later? (14) ______ , nine thirty? My sister's coming over for dinner.
Alex: Fine. Why don't you bring her (15) ______ ? I haven't seen her for years.
Jim: OK, I'll see if she (16) ______ like it.
Alex: Great, nine thirty on Tuesday (17) ______ .
Jim: OK, looking forward (18) ______ it.
Alex: See you then. Bye.
Jim: Bye.

▶ 29 **Listen and check.**

WRITING

Writing an essay
Using concessive discourse markers

1 **Complete the sentences with the words in the box. Use each word or phrase once.**

another theory	despite	however
one theory	while	yet

a We all need sleep, ________________ no one knows precisely why we need it.

b ________________ many years of research, there is no consensus.

c ________________ is that sleep enables the brain to organize information.

d ________________ is that sleep allows the brain to have a period of rest.

e Some people can survive on just four hours of sleep a night. ________________ , most people need between six and nine hours a night.

f ________________ experts agree on the chemical cause of sleep, their opinions differ when it comes to why we sleep.

2 **You are going to write an essay that answers the question "Why do we dream?"**

- Use some or all of the notes below for your essay. Add any other information you like.
- Plan the order and the content of the paragraphs.
- Think about how to expand the notes into complete sentences, and how to connect the sentences and paragraphs.
- Try to use concessive and other discourse markers.
- Write your essay. You should write approximately 250 words.

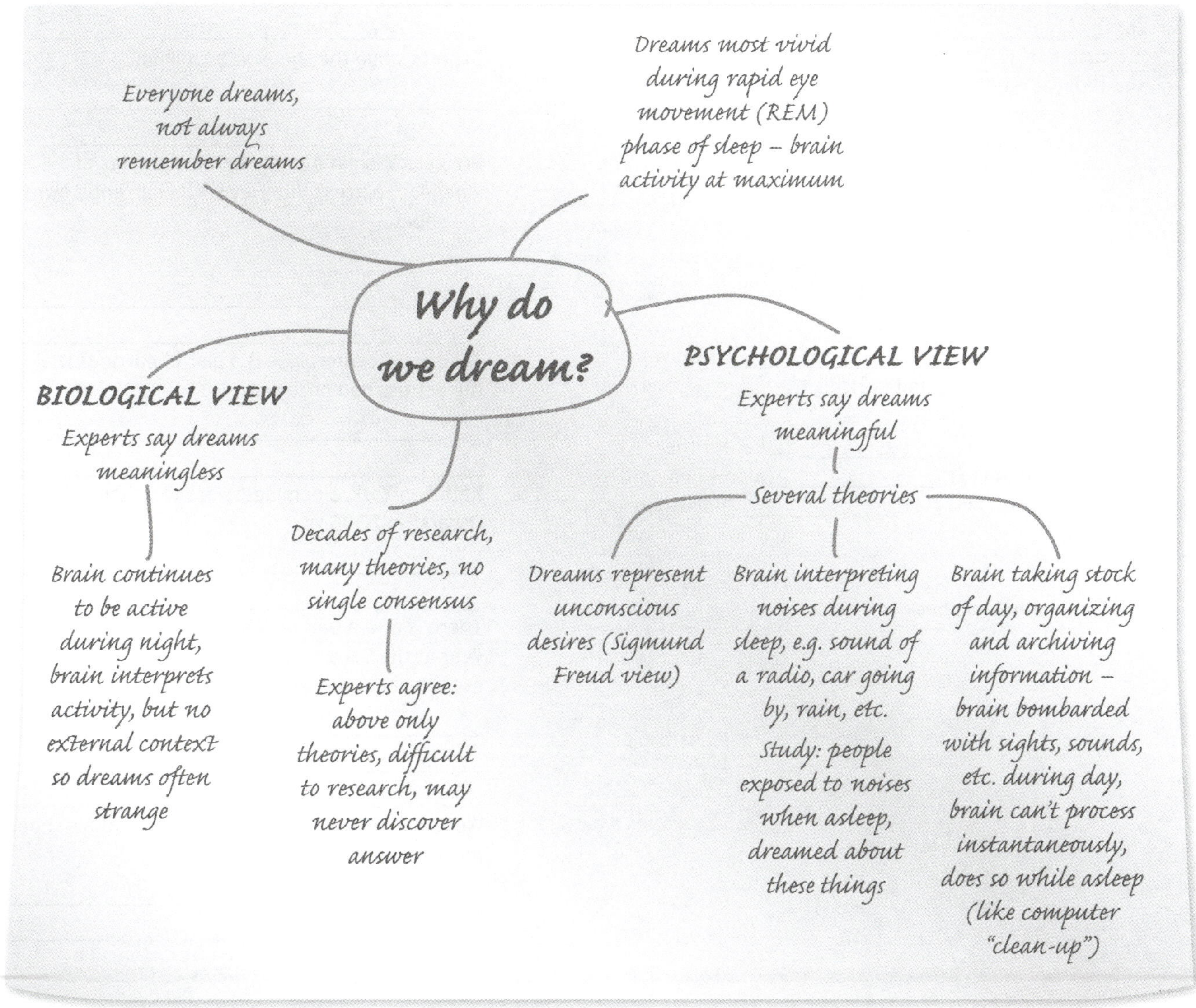

10 Footprints

GRAMMAR

1 **Complete the article by putting the verbs into the correct passive form. You do not need to use the auxiliary verb *be* in some cases.**

In the 1939 movie classic *The Wizard of Oz*, Dorothy (1) __is given__ (give) a pair of magical ruby slippers. In the original story, the shoes were silver, but they (2) ______________ (change) to ruby red to take advantage of the new Technicolor film process. The shoes have become one of the most iconic images from the movie.

It (3) ______________ (believe) that seven pairs of Dorothy's red slippers (4) ______________ (create) for the movie. Today, the whereabouts of only four pairs (5) ______________ (know).

One pair is in the Smithsonian Institution, two others (6) ______________ (own) by private collectors, and a fourth pair (7) ______________ (steal) in 2005 from the Judy Garland Museum and (8) ______________ (yet/be) recovered.

The last pair to come up for sale (9) ______________ (sell) at auction by Christie's for $666,000.

A pair of shoes which (10) ______________ (inspire) by Dorothy's ruby slippers (11) ____________________ (recently/put) on sale at Harrods department store in London with a price tag of over $3 million.

The red satin stilettos (12) ______________ (weave) from platinum thread and (13) ______________ (set) with 642 rubies.

After pictures (14) ______________ (take) for the press, the shoes (15) ______________ (place) in a bulletproof case and (16) ______________ (guard) at all times.

30 **Listen and check.**

2 **Rewrite the sentences using the passive form of the verbs. Omit the agent if this is not known, irrelevant, or obvious.**

The world's most expensive shoes

a US designer Stuart Weitzman made the world's most expensive shoes.
__The world's most expensive shoes were made by US designer Stuart Weitzman.__

b Experts value the shoes at $3 million.
____

c Princess Yasmin Aga Khan, the daughter of legendary actress Rita Hayworth, currently owns the shoes.
____

d The shoes' centerpiece is a pair of earrings that the actress had once worn.
____

e Kathleen York, a nominee, wore the shoes at the Oscars® in 2006.
____

f There is now a pair of Weitzman shoes every year at the Oscars®, and there is always great excitement about who will wear them.
____

g Weitzman has sold several other pairs of his shoes for over $1 million.
____

3 **Complete the text with the correct passive form of the verbs in the boxes. You do not need to use the auxiliary verb *be* in some cases.**

~~ever take~~ find make photograph

This is one of the most famous photographs (1) ___ever taken___ and shows what is perhaps the most famous footprint in history.

The footprint (2) ______________ and (3) ______________ by Buzz Aldrin during NASA's 1969 Apollo 11 mission as part of an experiment to study the nature of lunar dust.

The dust (4) ______________ to compact easily, leaving this iconic impression of the boot.

eventually erode leave make not disturb

Because there is no weather on the Moon, Aldrin's footprint (5) ______________ for millions of years until it (6) ______________ by micrometeorite impacts.

Footprints (7) ______________ on the Moon by a total of twelve astronauts, along with tire tracks (8) ______________ by the Lunar Rover vehicle in the later Apollo missions.

give finally discuss predict speak

Aldrin was in fact the second man to walk on the Moon, the honor of being the first (9) ______________ to Neil Armstrong, the mission commander. Aldrin, however, can claim the first words (10) ______________ from the Moon: "Tranquility Base. The Eagle has landed."

Today, over forty years later, the next generation of manned flights to the Moon (11) ______________ ______________. And it (12) ______________ ______________ that by 2030 there may even be human footprints on Mars.

4 **Complete the sentences comparing the countries' ecological footprints. Use each word or phrase in the box once.**

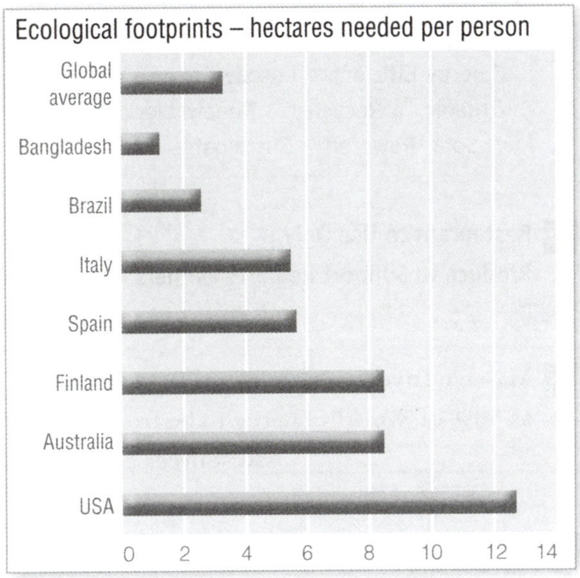

~~by far~~ considerably just nowhere near somewhat very slightly

a The USA's ecological footprint is ___by far___ the biggest of those shown.

b Spain's ecological footprint is ______________ bigger than Italy's.

c Finland's footprint is ______________ as big as Australia's.

d Brazil's footprint is ______________ less than the global average.

e Bangladesh's footprint is ______________ smaller than the other countries'.

f The other countries' ecological footprints are ______________ as big as the USA's.

5 **Write each sentence to show your own opinion. Use the words given and choose a word from the box.**

a little bit a little a lot ~~far~~ infinitely just much nowhere near slightly way

a soccer / baseball / exciting
Soccer is far more exciting than baseball.

b skiing / snowboarding / dangerous
____

c Brad Pitt / Johnny Depp / good-looking
____

d being happy / being rich / important
____

e playing computer games / shopping / fun
____

f writing English / speaking English / easy
____

VOCABULARY

1 Complete the news headlines with the words in the box.

Energy-Efficient	~~Locally Grown~~	
Organic	Recycled	Renewable
Solar-Powered	Sustainable	

a **Restaurant to Use Only** *Locally Grown* **Produce to Support Region's Farmers**

b Massive Investment in Wind Power as 50% of World's Energy to be from ________ Resources by 2050

c **Not Enough Sun in North-West for ________ Cars Say Experts**

d Sales of ________ Produce Fall During Economic Crisis

e **New ________ Washing Machine to Cost One Cent per Wash**

f ________ Tourism is Only Way to Avoid Loss of Minority Groups

g Glossy Magazine Industry Urged to Use ________ Paper

2 Match the sentence beginnings (a–i) with their endings (1–9).

a I put
b I have itchy
c I've got one
d I waited on him
e It would be nice to
f I started off
g I got cold
h I put my
i I need to stand on

1 put my feet up.
2 foot in the door.
3 my foot down.
4 foot in my mouth.
5 hand and foot.
6 feet.
7 my own two feet.
8 feet.
9 on the wrong foot.

a	b	c	d	e	f	g	h	i
3								

3 Complete the dialogues with the words in the box.

arm	defeatist	do	gained	~~go~~
good	happy	know	point	
try	twisted	ventured	want	

a A: Do you think I ought to apply for the job?
B: Yeah, I think you should *go* for it.

b A: Aaarrgh! I'll never get it right!
B: Don't be ________! Of course you will.

c A: I'm sure I won't be able to fix the computer myself.
B: It's worth giving it a ________.

d A: I'm not sure about going out tonight. And I can't really afford it anyway.
B: Go ahead, it'll ________ you ________.

e A: I really shouldn't have dessert. I'm trying to lose some weight.
B: Come on, you ________ you ________ to.

f A: Come on, come with us.
B: Oh, all right, you ________ my ________.

g A: I'd much rather go for pizza. I'm not in the mood for Chinese food.
B: OK then, if it'll make you ________.

h A: You should talk to your boss if you're unhappy.
B: What's the ________? He never listens.

i A: I'm sure he won't want to go out with me. What's the point of asking him?
B: Well, nothing ________, nothing ________.

31 **Listen and check.**

PRONUNCIATION

1 32 **Listen to these sentences and <u>underline</u> the most stressed word in each sentence.**

a Russia is far bigger than China.
b The book is way better than the movie.

2 **Which do you think is the most stressed word in each sentence?**

a Computer games are way better than they used to be.
b The movie is nowhere near as good as the book.
c Canada is only slightly bigger than the USA.
d Soccer is definitely not as popular as baseball.
e The bus is only a little cheaper than the train.
f Computers are infinitely more user-friendly these days.

33 **Listen and check. Repeat the sentences.**

LISTENING

1 34 **Cover the listening script on the right and listen to a radio show with Hannah, who backpacked around Vietnam. As you listen, put the following topics into the order in which she talks about them.**

a The places she visited ☐
b The impact of tourists ☐
c The Vietnamese people ☐
d Her first impressions of Vietnam ☐
e How she traveled around the country ☐

2 Answer the questions. Listen again to check.

a Hannah's first impressions of Vietnam were generally:
1 positive 2 negative 3 indifferent

b Hannah was surprised that Saigon was so:
1 modern 2 busy 3 interesting

c Tourists in Vietnam tend to:
1 stay in just one place 2 take different routes
3 take the same route

d Traveling around Vietnam is:
1 frustrating 2 easy 3 difficult

e How does Hannah feel about visiting "minority" villages?
1 She thinks it is fine.
2 She thinks we shouldn't do it.
3 She thinks it is both a good and a bad thing.

f Circle the words that describe the Vietnamese people, according to Hannah.
caring happy helpful unhelpful
indifferent delicate welcoming
relaxed friendly

3 Hannah says, "I would suggest the 'leave only footprints' motto." What does she mean by this?

____

____

4 Complete these expressions from the listening script with the words in the box. What do the expressions mean? Listen again and check.

atmosphere	bustle	by	out	path	place

a hustle and __________
b a happening __________
c a well-trodden __________
d worth checking __________
e soak up the __________
f watch the world go __________

Interviewer Hannah, what were your first impressions of Vietnam?

Hannah I was amazed from the minute I arrived in Saigon. The city is huge, jammed with traffic and people on the move everywhere. The backpacker area was really a happening place with lots of hustle and bustle. It's a very exciting city, and there's so much to see and do in Saigon. And it's really modern, which I wasn't expecting.

Interviewer And you traveled around the country, didn't you?

Hannah Yes, from south to north. It's a long, narrow country, so the route you take is pretty well determined for you. It's a well-trodden path, and you keep seeing the same faces all the time. The best way to get around is by bus. You can hop on and off along the way whenever and wherever you like - it's very well set up. For me the highlights were Hue, which, if you're interested in the Vietnam War, then this is the place to get your fix. And I loved Hanoi, the capital, which is a beautiful city and much more unspoiled than Saigon - there are lots of amazing little markets that are definitely worth checking out. It's the perfect place to soak up the atmosphere and watch the world go by. From there we went to Sapa, in the very north, which has some great walks in the hills through lots of tiny "minority" villages.

Interviewer Your experiences of "minority" villages in Vietnam were mixed. Tell us a little about this.

Hannah Well, this whole issue is very delicate. As tourists we want to find the "authentic" thing - remote, untouched, traditional villages. Yet, the moment that tourists go to such places we affect them and disrupt the authenticity. It's a real dilemma though, because visiting these villages generates money for the people who live there.

Interviewer So how can backpackers ensure that they don't have a negative impact on villagers?

Hannah I would suggest the "leave only footprints" motto and don't give money directly to people because it does affect the local economy on a dramatic scale. It's important to support sustainable tourism, leaving the minimum possible impact on the society that you have infiltrated.

Interviewer And finally, if it's possible to generalize, what are the Vietnamese people like?

Hannah I found them to be very easygoing and friendly. I think that the Buddhist religion encourages that. Lots of good karma. Most people along the way were very happy to help us, and we felt very welcome at all times.

11 Words

GRAMMAR

1 Look at the text below. Match the words in bold (1–12) with the words or phrases (a–i) they have been substituted for. Some words and phrases may be used more than once.

Do you write text messages? I'm sure you (1) **do**. Everyone (2) **does** these days. But do you think (3) **they** affect the way you read and write? Many literacy experts think they (4) **can** - and (5) **do**, especially among adolescents. (6) **They** argue that text messages, and in particular the shorthand used to write (7) **them**, can damage young people's reading and writing skills. The disregard for conventional grammar and spelling shown in (8) **them** is seen as a threat. However, (9) **others** argue that reading and writing SMS messages requires a sophisticated knowledge of the rules underlying the language. It is certainly true that since text messages became popular, young people have started writing much more than they ever (10) **did** (11) **before**. And writing has taken on a new importance in people's lives. It's now cool to (12) **do it**. And texting is especially cool.

a affect the way we write
b before SMS messages were invented
c literacy experts
d text messages
e texting
f write(s) text messages
g writing text messages
h write
i wrote

1	2	3	4	5	6	7	8	9	10	11	12
f											

2 Look at the conversation below. Make it as short as possible. Use substitution where necessary.

A: It's Tom's 30th ~~birthday party~~ tonight. Are you going ~~to the party~~? If ~~you're going to the party~~ so, I can give you a ride.

B: Where is the party taking place?

A: The party's taking place at his brother's bar, I think.

B: Nobody told me anything about the party. Maybe I haven't been invited to go to the party. Are you going?

A: Yes, Tom invited me to the party last week when I saw Tom at the golf club. We were both at the golf club with our bosses. Our bosses play golf together every Thursday.

B: I didn't know your boss played with Tom's boss. How long have they been playing golf together every week?

A: They've been playing together for as long as I can remember. Anyway, going back to Tom's party, you should definitely come. I'm sure Tom will be disappointed if you don't come to his party. I'll see you at Tom's party.

35 **Listen and compare your version with the recording.**

PRONUNCIATION

1 36 **Listen to these short exchanges. Cross out any words you don't actually hear.**

A: Are you ready to go out?
B: No, not yet, I'm just finishing this piece of work.
A: OK, we'll meet you there, then.
B: Yeah, I'll be there in about half an hour.
A: OK. We'll catch you later!

A: Did you see John last night?
B: No, was he supposed to be there?
A: As far as I know, yes.
B: Hmm. He must have gotten caught up at work or something.
A: I guess so.

2 37 **Listen again and repeat.**

VOCABULARY

1 **Match the words on the left with the words on the right to form compound nouns.**

a	always	1	consumption
b	conspicuous	2	crunch
c	credit	3	down time
d	digital	4	effect
e	face	5	connected
f	lipstick	6	time

2 **Complete the sentences using the compound nouns from Exercise 1.**

a Life has certainly become more stressful with the always connected lifestyle that most business people live these days.

b The ____________ means that consumers buy small luxury items rather than splurge on expensive indulgences.

c The store owners are the first to suffer in a ____________, with shoppers cutting back on expenditure across the board.

d Flashy cars, fur coats, and diamond-coated cell phones are all hallmarks of the super rich and their ____________ .

e It's really important to make sure you fit in some quality ____________ when you turn off your cell phone, unplug your laptop, and just relax.

f At the end of a long day in front of my computer screen, I really appreciate simple, old-fashioned ____________ with the people I love!

3 **Choose the correct prefix or suffix from the box to complete the definitions.**

~~ing~~ er click cyber fish ie

a stream__ing__: getting video through the internet before the entire video has been downloaded

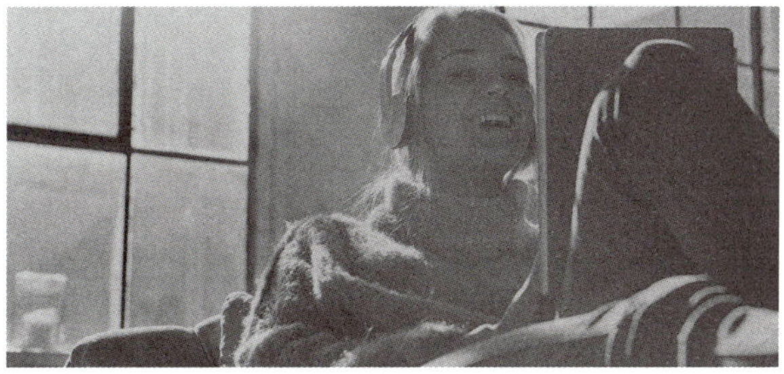

b ________bait: a link on a website that is designed to catch people's attention and encourage them to click

c cat________: to trick someone online by adopting a fake identity

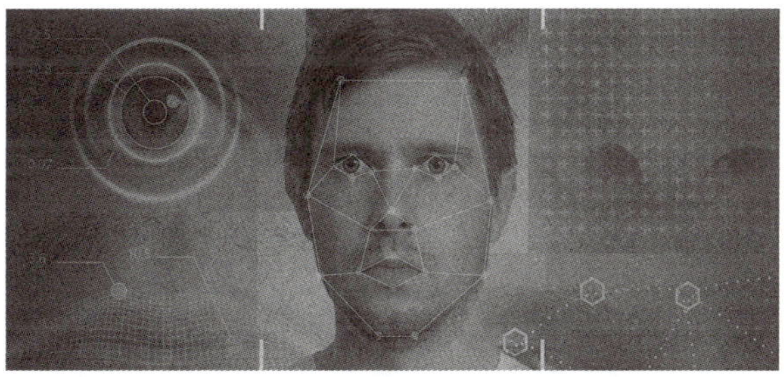

d brows________: a computer program that allows you to look at and search through information on the internet

e ________bully: somebody who uses the internet to frighten or upset another person

f self________: a photo that you take of yourself, usually for use in social media

4 **Replace the words in italics with the words and phrases in the box.**

favor	~~glean~~	going around in circles
got his point across	hit the right note	
rambling	sank in	tangents

a Younger users tend to *pick up* information from visual sources much quicker than older users. glean

b Most teenagers *give preference to* texting over speaking. ____________

c When writing an essay, remember to answer the question and do not go off on unnecessary *explanations or descriptions that are irrelevant to the topic.* ____________

d The plot is interesting, but her style is marred by long, *endless, and pointless* sentences that seem to go nowhere. ____________

e Stop *avoiding the issue* and get to the point! ____________

f I think he *explained himself* very succinctly. ____________

g Good job! You really managed to *create the right effect* - encouraging without being too patronizing. ____________

h He watched the expression on her face change as the meaning of his words slowly *was absorbed.* ____________

5 **Use the same word to complete both phrases in each pair.**

1 a You're twisting my _______ .

b You're deliberately misconstruing my _______ .

2 a My _______ is ...

b You're missing the _______ .

3 a I'm just _______ , ...

b What I'm _______ is ...

4 a That's not _______ I'm saying.

b So _______ are you implying?

5 a _______ is not what I meant.

b I didn't say _______ !

WRITING

Writing a cover letter
Cover letter conventions
Spelling

1 **Look at this checklist of things to remember when writing an email to accompany a job application. Put a check (✓) for the *dos* and a cross (✗) for the *don'ts*.**

a forget to use paragraphs to separate the three sections of your letter ☐
b use contracted forms or abbreviations ☐
c be as polite as you would if you were meeting the person for the first time ☐
d include irrelevant information ☐
e use a spellchecker and proofread your letter carefully ☐
f use the subject line to explain why you are writing ☐
g duplicate information included in your résumé ☐
h attach your résumé in a separate document ☐
i leave the recipient's name out and/or forget to sign your name as in a normal letter ☐
j be as chatty or informal as you would in an email to a friend ☐
k explain which post you are applying for ☐
l keep it brief and to the point ☐

2 **Read this email cover letter and answer the questions.**

a What position is the person applying for?
b What points on the checklist above (a–l) has he forgotten?

From: Robbie
To: staffing@dunroe.com
Subject: post of freelance translator
Attachment: Robbie's résumé

I'm writing to aply for the post of freelance translator advertised in the *Washington Post* on February 27th. I graduated in English and Europaen Studies at the University of Illinois in 1996. After graduating I worked for six months as a traine in a local trade journal but decided that I didn't like the job and left to study for my translator exams. I passed these in June 1997 and then wnet on to work for a series of small translation agencies in my hometown.

I am curently looking for a more permenent position which will allow me to improve my skils and develop as a translator. I think your company will benefit form my expereince and my abilities. I am available for an interveiw any time next week.

That's all for now,

Robbie

3 **Find and correct ten typos or spelling mistakes in the email.**

__________ __________
__________ __________
__________ __________
__________ __________
__________ __________

4 **Underline the phrases Robbie uses to explain:**

a why he's writing.
b why he's interested in the post.
c what he has to offer.
d when he can attend an interview.

5 **You are going to apply for the same job as Robbie. Write a cover letter to accompany your résumé. Invent any information you need to. Use the format below to help you. You should write approximately 250 words.**

Dear Mr./Ms. Last Name: (*If you don't know their name:* Dear Sir or Madam:)

First paragraph

Why you are writing

Remember to make a clear reference to the post you are applying for.

Notes ______________________________

____

____

Middle paragraphs

1 *Why you are interested*
Remember to include a short description of your current work position.

Notes ______________________________

____

____

2 *What you have to offer*
Convince the reader that you are a suitable candidate and that he/she should call you for an interview. Make connections between your abilities and the job requirements in the advertisement.

Notes ______________________________

____

____

Final paragraph

Remember to let the reader know when you are available for interview and how best to get in touch with you. Include a phone number and times when you can be reached at it.

Notes ______________________________

____

____

Sincerely,
Your name

12 Conscience

GRAMMAR

1 Match the sentences (a–g) with the responses (1–7).

a I really am fed up with always footing the bill.

b We're running a little late.

c She is really tired and needs a break.

d My car keeps breaking down.

e His grades are getting worse.

f John really doesn't have the experience to run the project.

g I don't agree with giving money to charities.

1 I wish I could spend more time with him to help him with his studies.
2 I'd rather we recruited someone with more of a background in this area.
3 I think it's time we got going.
4 It's high time he learned to pay his own way.
5 If only I had the money to buy a new one.
6 I'd rather people volunteered some of their time.
7 It's time she took a vacation.

a	b	c	d	e	f	g
4						

2 Correct the mistakes in these sentences.

a I'm really out of shape. I think it's time I ~~join~~ joined a gym.
b She'd rather spent the weekend in the countryside than in a busy city.
c I wish I don't have to work today. I'm feeling really tired.
d If only there wouldn't be so much bureaucracy involved in charity work.
e She wishes she can come with us on vacation, but her work commitments are going to keep her at home.
f I'd rather you not do that. It might be dangerous.
g It really is high time the government would do something more concrete to help the homeless.
h He said he'd rather I might give the presentation, as I've done it before and I know what's needed.

3 **Complete the second sentence so that it means the same as the first.**

a I really think the town should do something about the traffic.

It's time *the town did something about the the traffic.*

b Please don't speak so loud in my car.

I'd rather ________________________________

c I think someone needs to teach him a few manners. He's very rude.

It's high time ________________________________

d I really think he should stop wasting time and get a job.

It's about time ________________________________

e I'd prefer you to stay at home and take care of the children so that I can go shopping.

I'd rather ________________________________

PRONUNCIATION

1 38 **Listen to four responses to this comment. Mark the main stress in each one.**

So, I hear you did a parachute jump for charity.

a No, I did a bungee jump.
b No, that was my sister, not me.
c No, I did it for fun.
d No, but I'm thinking of doing one.

Why does the stress fall on these words?

2 **Look at the four responses below. Where does the main stress fall in each one?**

So, you were collecting money for the Red Cross.

a No, for Comic Relief, actually.
b No, we were collecting old clothes.
c No, I was sick that day, but my brother went.
d No, for our school, actually.

39 **Listen and check.**

VOCABULARY

1 Decide which word doesn't belong in each list (a–c) and then choose the correct explanation (1–3) for your answers.

a homeless person street performer wino
b beggar street vendor street windshield washer
c bag lady hobo street person

1 It's more formal than the other two.
2 It's informal; the other two are formal.
3 They don't do anything to earn the money they're given.

2 Underline the correct verb.

a The families were finally **reunited** / **secured** last night after three harrowing days of uncertainty.
b The course seeks to help trainees **represent** / **secure** employment in the airline industry.
c It's high time the government started **addressing** / **pursuing** the issue of teenage drinking, before we become a nation of alcoholics!
d More and more women are choosing to **pursue** / **represent** a career in previously male-dominated fields such as engineering.
e It is an immense honor to be called to **boost** / **represent** my country in the Olympics®.
f Winning that prize in the dance competition has really helped **address** / **boost** her self-esteem. She's much happier now.

3 Complete the sentences with the words in the box.

a a ~~clear~~ ease good guilty her in my on

a I know I didn't have anything to do with it. I have _a_ _clear_ conscience.
b I can't see how she'll ever forget the incident. It'll be _________ _________ conscience forever.
c _________ _________ conscience, can you really say that when you see people begging for money on the street, you don't feel bad?
d Thanks for dropping by and checking on my grandmother. It helps _________ _________ conscience. I'm worried about her living by herself.
e She's suffering from _________ _________ conscience. She knows it was her fault and feels terrible.

4 Write the words in the correct order to make apologies. Add punctuation.

a sorry really I'm again happen won't It
I'm really sorry. It wont happen again.
b apology you think an I owe I
____
c seat idea your Sorry was I no had this
____
d mind my sorry slipped I'm totally it
____
e sorry am really I idea I no had
____
f bad weather We all trains canceled have been to inform regret you due to that
____
____

5 Match the apologies from Exercise 4 with the responses (1–6) below.

1 Again! They're always doing this to me!
2 It better not! We can't afford another mistake like that!
3 It's OK. You can stay there. It doesn't really matter.
4 You most certainly do!
5 That's OK. You couldn't have known.
6 It's OK. It wasn't important.

a	b	c	d	e	f
2					

40 **Listen and check.**

LISTENING

1 41 **Cover the listening script on the right and listen to a radio show with a volunteer worker for a non-profit organization called Comic Relief. Answer these questions.**

a When was the organization founded? ___________

b Why was it founded? ___________

____

____

c Why is it called "Comic Relief"? ___________

____

d What's the name of the main event organized by Comic Relief? ___________

e What kinds of activities do the fundraisers get involved in? ___________

____

2 Which of these topics are *not* discussed?

a the people who founded the organization

b the main difference between Comic Relief and other non-profit organizations

c the amount of money raised

d the projects funded by the charity

e the main fundraising events

f the celebrities who support the cause

Listen to the interview again to check.

3 Complete the extracts below with the words in the box.

catchy	devastating	good	organized	refugee	role	silly

a At the time there was a ___________ famine in Sudan and Ethiopia.

b The charity was launched from a ___________ camp in Sudan ...

c Yes, the appeal of doing something silly for a ___________ cause is very powerful.

d ... basically, we were looking around for a ___________ symbol ...

e ... people love the sponsored ___________ -reversal events – bosses get sponsored to be a secretary for the day ...

f ... then there are the ___________ events, like fun runs ...

g ... with thousands of runners jogging in various ___________ costumes.

Interviewer	Today, in the studio, we're pleased to welcome Janet Whittall, a volunteer for the non-profit organization, Comic Relief. Hello, Janet. Thanks for being with us here today.
Janet	It's a pleasure.
Interviewer	So, could you tell us a little bit of the history behind Comic Relief? When did it first start up?
Janet	It first started up in 1985. At the time there was a devastating famine in Sudan and Ethiopia. The organization was set up from a refugee camp in Sudan on Christmas Day to raise funds for the victims of the famine. But they also wanted to look at the more widespread needs of the poor in that region, and indeed of poor and disadvantaged people all over the world.
Interviewer	But why "Comic Relief"? What's the story behind the name?
Janet	Well, basically, it's called Comic Relief because it was first set up by comedians, and because it uses comedy and laughter to get its message across. That's what makes it unique.
Interviewer	And it's been incredibly successful.
Janet	Yes, the appeal of doing something silly for a good cause is very powerful. Did you know that in 2009 more than $121 million was raised on Red Nose Day?
Interviewer	How did the idea for Red Nose Day come to be?
Janet	Well, basically, we were looking around for a catchy symbol, something that would be cheap and easy for everyone to use. And the traditional red nose worn by circus clowns really fits the bill – on Red Nose Day you can see them everywhere, not only on people's faces. You see them stuck on the front of cars, buses, and even subway trains.
Interviewer	But there's more to Red Nose Day than wearing red noses.
Janet	Yes, there's all kinds of sponsored silliness going on. People love the sponsored role-reversal events – bosses get sponsored to be a secretary for the day, or students sponsor their teachers to wear their school uniform – and then there are organized events, like the fun runs, with thousands of runners jogging in various silly costumes.
Interviewer	So, what will you be doing on Red Nose Day this year?
Janet	We're holding a huge Red Party downtown. Everyone has to dress in red, bring along some red food, and of course pay a generous check which will all go to Comic Relief. What about you?
Interviewer	The staff here at the radio station has sponsored me to shave my head and have it painted red.

Notes

Notes

Notes

Notes

Notes